SCHOLASTIC

100 SCIENCE LESSONS

Terms and conditions

IMPORTANT – PERMITTED USE AND WARNINGS – READ CAREFULLY BEFORE USING

IF YOU ACCEPT THE ABOVE CONDITIONS YOU MAY PROCEED TO USE THE CD-ROM.

Recommended system requirements:

- Windows: XP (Service Pack 3), Vista (Service Pack 2), Windows 7 or Windows 8 with 2.33GHz processor
- Mac: OS 10.6 to 10.8 with Intel Core™ Duo processor
- 1GB RAM (recommended)
- 1024 x 768 Screen resolution
- CD-ROM drive (24x speed recommended)
- 16-bit sound card
- Adobe Reader (version 9 recommended for Mac users)
- Broadband internet connections (for installation and updates)

For all technical support queries, please phone Scholastic Customer Services on 0845 6039091.

Book End, Range Road, Witney, Oxfordshire, OX29 0YD
www.scholastic.co.uk

© 2014, Scholastic Ltd

1 2 3 4 5 6 7 8 9   4 5 6 7 8 9 0 1 2 3

British Library Cataloguing-in-Publication Data
A catalogue record for this book is available from the
British Library.

ISBN 978-1407-12769-9
Printed by Bell & Bain Ltd, Glasgow

Due to the nature of the web we cannot guarantee
the content or links of any site mentioned. We strongly
recommend that teachers check websites before using
them in the classroom.

Extracts from *The National Curriculum in England, Science
Programme of Study* © Crown Copyright. Reproduced
under the terms of the Open Government Licence
(OGL). http://www.nationalarchives.gov.uk/doc/open-
government-licence/open-government-licence.htm

Authors
Adelene Cogill, Julie Cogill, Clifford Hibbard,
Paul Hollin, Peter Riley

Consultant
Juliet Gladston

Series Editor
Peter Riley

Editorial team
Rachel Morgan, Pollyanna Poulter,
Melissa Somers, Juliet Gladston

Cover Design
Andrea Lewis

Design Team
Sarah Garbett, Shelley Best and Andrea Lewis

CD-ROM development
Hannah Barnett, Phil Crothers, MWA Technologies
Private Ltd

Typesetting
Tracey Camden

Illustrations
Tomek.gr

Contents

Introduction

About the series

The *100 Science Lessons* series is designed to meet the requirements of the 2014 Curriculum, Science Programmes of Study. There are six books in the series, Years 1–6, and each book contains lesson plans, resources and ideas matched to the new curriculum. It can be a complex task to ensure that a progressive and appropriate curriculum is followed in all year groups; this series has been carefully structured to ensure that a progressive and appropriate curriculum is followed throughout.

About the new curriculum

The curriculum documentation for Science provides a single-year programme of study for each year in Key Stage 1 and 2. However schools are only required to teach the relevant programmes of study by the end of the key stage and can approach their curriculum planning with greater flexibility than ever before in the following ways. Within each key stage they can introduce content earlier or later than set out in the programme of study and they can introduce key stage content during an earlier key stage if appropriate. Whatever plan is used the school curriculum for science must be set out on a year-by-year basis and made available online.

Knowledge and conceptual understanding

The national curriculum for science aims to ensure that all children develop scientific knowledge and conceptual understanding through the specific disciplines of Biology (Plants, Animals including humans, Seasonal changes, Living things and their habitats, Evolution and inheritance), Chemistry (Everyday materials, Uses of everyday materials, Rocks, States of matter, Properties and changes of materials) and Physics (Seasonal changes, Light, Forces and magnets, Sound, Electricity, Earth and space). It is vitally important that the children develop a secure understanding of each key block of knowledge and its concepts in order to progress to the next stage. As they do so they should also be familiar with and use technical terminology accurately and precisely and build up an extended specialist vocabulary. Equally they should also apply their mathematical knowledge to their understanding of science including collecting, presenting and analysing data.

The nature, processes and methods of science

The requirements needed for the understanding of the nature, processes and methods of science are set out at the beginning of Key Stage 1, Lower Key Stage 2 and Upper Key Stage 2 in a section called Working scientifically. This section of the curriculum replaces the Science enquiry section of the previous science curriculum. It is important that Working scientifically is not taught as a separate strand and guidance is given in the non-statutory notes to help embed it in the scientific content of each area of the programme of study. In the working scientifically section the children are introduced to a range of types of scientific enquiry. These include observing over time, classifying and grouping, identifying, comparative and fair testing (making controlled investigations), pattern seeking and researching using secondary sources. The questions used to stimulate the enquiry should be answered by the children through collecting, presenting and analysing data and drawing conclusions from their findings.

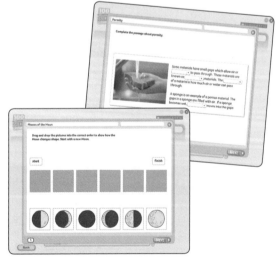

SCHOLASTIC

About the book

This book is divided into six chapters; each chapter contains a half-term's work and is based around one of the content areas in the programme of study. Each chapter follows the same structure:

Chapter introduction

At the start of each chapter there is an introduction with the following features. This includes:

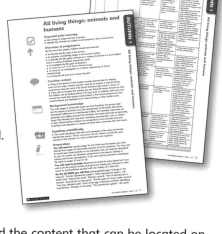

- **Expected prior learning:** What the children are expected to know before starting the work in the chapter.
- **Overview of progression:** A brief explanation of how the children progress through the chapter.
- **Creative context:** How the chapter could link to other curriculum areas.
- **Background knowledge:** A section explaining scientific terms and suchlike to enhance your subject knowledge, where required.
- **Speaking scientifically:** A section highlighting some of the key words featured in the chapter for building up the children's scientific vocabulary. This is also a feature of every lesson (see below).
- **Preparation:** Any resources required for the teaching of the chapter, including things that need to be sourced or prepared and the content that can be located on the CD-ROM. As part of the preparation of all practical work you should consult your school's policies on practical work and select activities for which you are confident to take responsibility. The ASE *Be Safe Forth Edition* gives very useful guidance on health and safety issues in primary science.
- **Chapter at a glance:** This is a table that summarises the content of each lesson, including: the curriculum objectives, lesson objectives, the main activity or activities and the working scientifically statutory requirements that are featured in each lesson.

Lessons

Each chapter contains six weeks' of lessons, each week contains three lessons. At the start of each half term there is an introductory lesson revisiting relevant content from work in previous years then introducing the new area of study. There is also a checkpoint section to check on the children's knowledge before proceeding to the next lesson.

All lessons including the introductory lesson have lesson plans that include the relevant combination of headings from below.

- **Lesson objectives:** A list of objectives for the lesson.
- **Resources:** What you require to teach the lesson.
- **Speaking scientifically:** A list of words to use in the lesson. The children should learn to spell them, understand their meanings and use them when talking about their activities, particularly when working scientifically.
- **Introduction:** A short and engaging activity to begin the lesson.
- **Whole-class work:** Working together as a class.

- **Group/Paired/Independent work:** Children working independently of the teacher in pairs, groups or alone.
- **Differentiation:** Ideas for how to support children who are struggling with a concept or how to extend those children who understand a concept without taking them onto new work.
- **Science in the wider world:** The information in this section may develop some of the content and concepts in the lesson and show how they relate to the wider world in their implications for humanity (such as health care) or impact on the environment (such as initiating conservation strategies).
- **Review:** A chance to review the children's learning and ensure the outcomes of the lesson have been achieved.

Assess and review

At the end of each chapter are activities for assessing and reviewing the children's understanding. These can be conducted during the course of the chapter's work, saved until the end of the chapter or done at a later date.

All assessment and review activities follow the same format:

- **Curriculum objectives:** These are the areas of focus for the assess and review activity. There may be one focus or more than one depending on the activity.
- **Resources:** What you require to conduct the activities.
- **Working scientifically:** Each activity features one or more of the Working scientifically objectives for assessment.
- **Revise:** A series of short activities or one longer activity to revise and consolidate the children's learning and ensure they understand the concept(s).
- **Assess:** An assessment activity to provide a chance for the children to demonstrate their understanding and for you to check this.
- **Further practice:** Ideas for further practice on the focus, whether children are insecure in their learning or you want to provide extra practice or challenge.

Photocopiable pages

At the end of each chapter are some photocopiable pages that will have been referred to in the lesson plans.

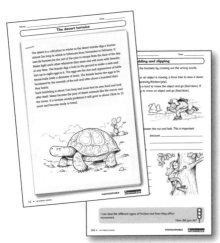

These sheets are for the children to use; there is generally a title, an instruction, an activity and an 'I can' statement at the bottom. These sheets are also provided on the CD-ROM alongside additional pages as referenced in the lessons (see page 7 About the CD-ROM). The children should be encouraged to complete the 'I can' statements by colouring in the traffic lights to say how they think they have done (red – not very well, amber – ok, green – very well).

About the CD-ROM

The CD-ROM contains:

- Printable versions of the photocopiable sheets from the book and additional photocopiable sheets as referenced in the lesson plans.
- Interactive activities for children to complete or to use on the whiteboard.
- Media resources to display.
- Printable versions of the lesson plans.
- Digital versions of the lesson plans with the relevant resources linked to them.

Getting started

- Put the CD-ROM into your CD-ROM drive.
  - For Windows users, the install wizard should autorun, if it fails to do so then navigate to your CD-ROM drive. Then follow the installation process.
  - For Mac users, copy the disk image file to your hard drive. After it has finished copying double-click it to mount the disk image. Navigate to the mounted disk image and run the installer. After installation the disk image can be unmounted and the DMG can be deleted from the hard drive.
- To complete the installation of the program you need to open the program and click 'Update' in the pop-up. Please note – this CD-ROM is web-enabled and the content will be downloaded from the internet to your hard-drive to populate the CD-ROM with the relevant resources. This only needs to be done on first use, after this you will be able to use the CD-ROM without an internet connection. If at any point any content is updated you will receive another pop-up upon start up with an internet connection.

Navigating the CD-ROM

There are two options to navigate the CD-ROM either as a Child or as a Teacher.

Child

- Click on the 'Child' button on the first menu screen.
- In the second menu click on the relevant class (please note only the books installed on the machine or network will be accessible. You can also rename year groups to match your school's naming conventions via the Teacher > Settings > Rename books area).
- A list of interactive activities will be displayed, children need to locate the correct one and click 'Go' to launch it.
- There is the opportunity to print or save a PDF of the activity at the end.

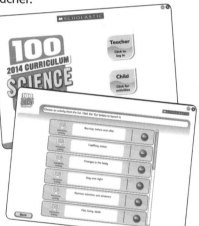

Teacher

- Click on the 'Teacher' button on the first menu screen and you will be taken to a screen showing which of the *100 English* books you have purchased. From here, you can also access information about getting started and the credits.
- To enter the product click 'Next' in the bottom right.
- You then need to enter a password (the password is: login).
- On first use:
  - Enter as a Guest by clicking on the 'Guest' button.
  - If desired, create a profile for yourself by adding your name to the list of users. Profiles allow you to save favourites and to specify which year group(s) you wish to be able to view.
  - Go to 'Settings' to create a profile for yourself – click 'Add user' and enter your name. Then choose the year groups you wish to have access to (you can return to this screen to change this at any time). Click on 'Login' at the top of the screen to re-enter the disk under your new profile.
- On subsequent uses you can choose your name from the drop-down list. The 'Guest' option will always be available if you, or a colleague, wish to use this.
- You can search the CD-ROM using the tools or save favourites.

For more information about how to use the CD-ROM, please refer to the help file which can be found in the teacher area of the CD-ROM. It is a red button with a question mark on it on the right-hand side of the screen just underneath the 'Settings' tab.

Curriculum grid

The tables below show the weekly curriculum coverage for each chapter.

Curriculum objectives	Autumn 1						Autumn 2					
	W1	W2	W3	W4	W5	W6	W1	W2	W3	W4	W5	W6
Living things and their habitats												
To describe the differences in the life cycles of a mammal, an amphibian, an insect and a bird	✓		✓	✓	✓	✓						
To describe the life process of reproduction in some plants and animals												
Animals, including humans												
To describe the changes as humans develop to old age	✓	✓										
Properties and changes of materials												
To compare and group together everyday materials on the basis of their properties							✓	✓				
To know that some materials will dissolve in liquid to form a solution, and to describe how to recover a substance from a solution											✓	✓
To use knowledge of solids, liquids and gases to decide how mixtures might be separated										✓	✓	✓
To give reasons, based on evidence from comparative and fair tests, for the particular uses of everyday materials									✓	✓		
To demonstrate that dissolving, mixing and changes of state are reversible changes											✓	✓
To explain that some changes result in the formation of new materials, and that this kind of change is not usually reversible												
Earth and space												
To describe the movement of the Earth, and other planets, relative to the Sun in the solar system												
To describe the movement of the Moon relative to the Earth												
To describe the Sun, Earth and Moon as approximately spherical bodies												
To use the idea of the Earth's rotation to explain day and night and the apparent movement of the Sun across the sky												
Forces												
To explain that unsupported objects fall towards the Earth because of the force of gravity acting between the Earth and the falling object												
To identify the effects of air resistance, water resistance and friction, that act between moving surfaces												
To recognise that some mechanisms, including levers, pulleys and gears, allow a smaller force to have a greater effect												

Curriculum objectives	Spring 1						Spring 2					
	W1	W2	W3	W4	W5	W6	W1	W2	W3	W4	W5	W6
Living things and their habitats												
To describe the differences in the life cycles of a mammal, an amphibian, an insect and a bird												✓
To describe the life process of reproduction in some plants and animals							✓	✓	✓	✓	✓	✓
Animals, including humans												
To describe the changes as humans develop to old age												
Properties and changes of materials												
To compare and group together everyday materials on the basis of their properties												
To know that some materials will dissolve in liquid to form a solution, and to describe how to recover a substance from a solution												
To use knowledge of solids, liquids and gases to decide how mixtures might be separated												
To give reasons, based on evidence from comparative and fair tests, for the particular uses of everyday materials												
To demonstrate that dissolving, mixing and changes of state are reversible changes												
To explain that some changes result in the formation of new materials, and that this kind of change is not usually reversible												
Earth and space												
To describe the movement of the Earth, and other planets, relative to the Sun in the solar system		✓	✓	✓		✓						
To describe the movement of the Moon relative to the Earth			✓	✓	✓							
To describe the Sun, Earth and Moon as approximately spherical bodies	✓				✓							
To use the idea of the Earth's rotation to explain day and night and the apparent movement of the Sun across the sky	✓	✓	✓									
Forces												
To explain that unsupported objects fall towards the Earth because of the force of gravity acting between the Earth and the falling object												
To identify the effects of air resistance, water resistance and friction, that act between moving surfaces												
To recognise that some mechanisms, including levers, pulleys and gears, allow a smaller force to have a greater effect												

Curriculum objectives	Summer 1						Summer 2					
	W1	W2	W3	W4	W5	W6	W1	W2	W3	W4	W5	W6
Living things and their habitats												
To describe the differences in the life cycles of a mammal, an amphibian, an insect and a bird												
To describe the life process of reproduction in some plants and animals												
Animals, including humans												
To describe the changes as humans develop to old age												
Properties and changes of materials												
To compare and group together everyday materials on the basis of their properties												
To know that some materials will dissolve in liquid to form a solution, and to describe how to recover a substance from a solution												
To use knowledge of solids, liquids and gases to decide how mixtures might be separated	✓											
To give reasons, based on evidence from comparative and fair tests, for the particular uses of everyday materials												
To demonstrate that dissolving, mixing and changes of state are reversible changes												
To explain that some changes result in the formation of new materials, and that this kind of change is not usually reversible	✓	✓	✓	✓	✓	✓						
Earth and space												
To describe the movement of the Earth, and other planets, relative to the Sun in the solar system												
To describe the movement of the Moon relative to the Earth												
To describe the Sun, Earth and Moon as approximately spherical bodies												
To use the idea of the Earth's rotation to explain day and night and the apparent movement of the Sun across the sky												
Forces												
To explain that unsupported objects fall towards the Earth because of the force of gravity acting between the Earth and the falling object							✓	✓				
To identify the effects of air resistance, water resistance and friction, that act between moving surfaces							✓		✓	✓	✓	
To recognise that some mechanisms, including levers, pulleys and gears, allow a smaller force to have a greater effect												✓

All living things: animals and humans

Expected prior learning
- Use of keys to assign animals to groups.
- Identify how animals are suited to and adapted to their environment.

Overview of progression
By the end of this chapter children should have learned:
- to describe the life cycle of the human
- to sequence and identify stages in the human timeline
- to describe the life cycles common to a variety of animals in a local habitat and in a variety of habitats around the world
- to investigate the life cycle of dinosaurs
- to study the work of Sir David Attenborough
- to carry out an investigation on a theme explored by Sir David Attenborough
- to study the life and work of Jane Goodall

Creative context
- Many of the lessons in this chapter provide opportunities for display work but the major creative exercise could be to prepare a natural history programme using the work of Sir David Attenborough (week 5, lesson 3).
- If you wish to develop this activity you can bring this lesson forward so that the children can be thinking about it as they work on habitats, both local and around the world. Each group could produce a five-minute programme that could be filmed and displayed at an open evening or other similar event.

Background knowledge
The main stages of animal life cycles are birth/hatching, the young stage and the degree of parental care, the development of the adults and sexual dimorphism (difference in male/female bodies). For example, male birds are generally more highly-coloured than females, and male mammals are generally larger than females and may have secondary characteristics, such as antlers in deer. Metamorphism needs to be recognised in some animals (frog and butterfly), and migration is a feature of some birds, mammals, fish and insects.

Speaking scientifically
- The words describing main parts and processes of the male and female reproductive system. Words connected with the habitat and the life cycle activities of the animals in it, such as *hibernation* and *migration*.

Preparation
You will need to: examine page 34 and make sure the lessons you have selected from pages 23–28 provide answers to all the questions. You may wish to consult your school policies on sex education and use materials developed for part of a school sex education programme in the lessons relating to puberty and human reproduction. A zoo visit could be planned to investigate the topics on pages 22 and 24–26.

You will need to provide: Resources are listed for every lesson but if you wish to do the creative activity of programme making you will need to have access to, and familiarise yourself with, the making of a video film.

On the CD-ROM you will find: photocopiable pages 'Changes in the body (2)', 'Female reproductive system', 'Male reproductive system', 'Life before birth', 'Map of the world', 'Dinosaur growth', 'Test of reproduction in humans', 'Song thrush survival game', 'The life cycle of a frog'; media resource 'Tree frog', 'Banded snails', 'Parts of the egg'; interactive activities 'Identifying invertebrates', 'Changes in the body', 'The reproductive system', 'Life cycles'

Chapter at a glance

Week	Lesson	Curriculum objectives	Lesson objectives	Main activity	Working scientifically
1	1	• (Y4) To identify and name a variety of living things in the local and wider environment. • To describe the life cycles common to a variety of animals.	• To review the animals that live in the local environment. • To review the use of keys in assigning animals to groups. • To begin to consider life cycles.	Exploring the life cycles of local animals and animals from around the world. Gathering evidence of life cycles.	• Exploring and using classification keys to help group, identify and name a variety of living things in their local and wider environment. • Identifying scientific evidence that has been used to support or refute ideas or arguments.
	2	• To describe the changes as humans develop to old age.	• To know that human bodies vary naturally. • To know that humans have a growth spurt. • To know that parts of the body change in proportion to growth.	Constructing a bar chart to show variation in growth in a class and a line graph from data provided.	• Recording data and results of increasing complexity using scientific diagrams and labels, classification keys, tables, bar and line graphs.
	3	• To describe the changes as humans develop to old age.	• To know about the changes that take place at puberty in males and females.	Using a photocopiable to learn about changes in both sexes at puberty.	• Identifying scientific evidence that has been used to support or refute ideas or arguments.
2	1	• To describe the changes as humans develop to old age.	• To know about the structure and function of the male and female reproductive systems.	Distinguishing the parts of the male and female reproductive systems using diagrams and labels.	• Identifying scientific evidence that has been used to support or refute ideas or arguments.
	2	• To describe the changes as humans develop to old age.	• To know about the development of the baby in the uterus.	Using diagrams and information to construct a sequence of the development of the baby in the uterus.	• Identifying scientific evidence that has been used to support or refute ideas or arguments.
	3	• To describe the changes as humans develop to old age.	• To understand the difference between a life cycle and a timeline. • To know and recognise the stages in the human timeline.	Sequencing the stages in the human time line and grouping a range of humans to their stage in the time line.	• Reporting and presenting findings from enquiries, including conclusions, causal relationships and explanations of and degree of trust in results, in oral and written forms such as displays and other presentations.
3	1	• To describe the differences in the life cycles of a mammal, an amphibian, an insect and a bird.	• To learn about the life cycles of mammals. • To research and present information about the three kinds of mammals.	Constructing a bar and a line graph relating to the development of mammals. Researching information about placental mammals, marsupial and egg laying mammals.	• Taking measurements, using a range of scientific equipment, with increasing accuracy and precision, taking repeat readings where appropriate. • Recording data and results of increasing complexity using scientific diagrams and labels, classification keys, tables, scatter graphs, bar and line graphs.
	2	• To describe the differences in the life cycles of a mammal, an amphibian, an insect and a bird.	• To learn about the life cycle of a bird. • To find out about the risks to survival during the life cycle.	Making a diagram of the components of an egg. Discovering the impact of environmental factors on survival.	• Recording data and results of increasing complexity using scientific diagrams and labels, classification keys, tables, scatter graphs, bar and line graphs.
	3	• To describe the differences in the life cycles of a mammal, an amphibian, an insect and a bird.	• To learn about the life cycle of a frog. • To learn about the different kinds of amphibians.	Sequencing detailed changes in the life cycle of a frog. Researching questions and presenting evidence.	• Reporting and presenting findings from enquiries, including conclusions, causal relationships and explanations of and degree of trust in results, in oral and written forms such as displays and other presentations. • Identifying scientific evidence that has been used to support or refute ideas or arguments.

Chapter at a glance

Week	Lesson	Curriculum objectives	Lesson objectives	Main activity	Working scientifically
4	1	• To describe the differences in the life cycles of a mammal, an amphibian, an insect and a bird.	• To learn about the life cycle of the butterfly. • To learn that some insects have nymph stages instead of caterpillar stages.	Constructing a life cycle of the butterfly and recording the increase in larva length. Comparing the life cycle of a butterfly with a grasshopper or locust.	• Taking measurements, using a range of scientific equipment, with increasing accuracy and precision, taking repeat readings where appropriate. • Recording data and results of increasing complexity using scientific diagrams and labels, classification keys, tables, scatter graphs, bar and line graphs.
	2	• To describe the differences in the life cycles of a mammal, an amphibian, an insect and a bird.	• To learn about the life cycle of a tree frog. • To learn about the life cycles of rainforest animals.	Investigating how a resonator works. Researching rainforest animals' life cycles.	• Planning different types of scientific enquiries to answer questions, including recognising and controlling variables where necessary.
	3	• To describe the differences in the life cycles of a mammal, an amphibian, an insect and a bird.	• To know the zones of the ocean. • To know the life cycle of a marine creature.	Plotting the movement of the eel, sequencing its life cycle, describing how it changes. Researching the life cycles of sea creatures.	• Identifying scientific evidence that has been used to support or refute ideas or arguments.
5	1	• To describe the differences in the life cycles of a mammal, an amphibian, an insect and a bird.	• To learn about the life cycles of desert animals.	Modelling the desert tortoise life cycle. Researching life cycles of desert animals.	• Using simple models to describe scientific ideas.
	2	• To describe the differences in the life cycles of a mammal, an amphibian, an insect and a bird.	• To learn about the life cycles of dinosaurs. • To understand how the activities of living animals can help explain the fossil evidence of extinct ones.	Constructing a dinosaur nest site. Investigating dinosaur growth.	• Recording data and results of increasing complexity using scientific diagrams and labels, classification keys, tables, scatter graphs, bar and line graphs.
	3	• To find out about the work of naturalists and animal behaviourists such as Sir David Attenborough.	• To learn about the life of Sir David Attenborough. • To learn about a favourite animal.	Researching and presenting the life cycle of an animal in a way that is interesting to others.	• Reporting and presenting findings from enquiries, including conclusions, causal relationships and explanations of and degree of trust in results, in oral and written forms such as displays and other presentations.
6	1	• To find out about the work of naturalists and animal behaviourists such as Sir David Attenborough.	• To learn about the effect of camouflage.	Investigating the camouflage of model snail shells.	• Planning different types of scientific enquiries to answer questions, including recognising and controlling variables where necessary. • Reporting and presenting findings from enquiries, including conclusions, causal relationships and explanations of and degree of trust in results, in oral and written forms such as displays and other presentations.
	2	• To find out about the work of naturalists and animal behaviourists such as Dame Jane Goodall.	• To learn about the life of Dame Jane Goodall.	Comparing their own early interests in animals with those of Dame Jane Goodall. Writing an account of animal behaviour from observations made.	• Reporting and presenting findings from enquiries, including conclusions, causal relationships and explanations of and degree of trust in results, in oral and written forms such as displays and other presentations.
	3	• To find out about the work of naturalists and animal behaviourists such as Dame Jane Goodall.	• To learn about the work of Dame Jane Goodall at Gombe National Park. • To learn about the Jane Goodall Institute.	Preparing a plan to improve the local environment for wildlife. Monitoring changes in the environment.	• Recording data and results of increasing complexity using scientific diagrams and labels, classification keys, tables, scatter graphs, bar and line graphs.
Assess and review					

Objectives
• To review the animals that live in the local environment.
• To review the use of keys in assigning animals to groups.
• To begin to consider life cycles.

Resources
Photocopiable page 36 'Identifying invertebrates'; interactive activity 'Identifying invertebrates'; photographs of invertebrates (such as an earthworm, slug, snail, woodlouse, millipede, centipede, beetle and spider); paper and pencils

Speaking scientifically
habitat, ecologist, evergreen, deciduous, invertebrate, vertebrate, life cycles, life span

Lesson 1: What do we know about life cycles?

Previous knowledge required
The children should have studied a local habitat (preferably one with bushes and trees for this lesson) in earlier years from which they can recall observations of the plants and animals found there.

Introduction
Display the collection of photographs and explain to the children that you are beginning a new topic and that you want to find out what ideas the children already have. Explain that the topic is about animals and the places where they live. Give them a few minutes to explore the pictures.

Whole-class work
1. Ask: *What do we call the home of living things?* (a habitat) Ask the children to describe a local habitat. During the discussion build up notes on the board using the following headings: 'The ground' (a description of the soil – black, brown, sandy, presence of rocks, well drained or soggy, presence or absence of dead leaves), 'The plants closest to the ground' (mosses, short grass, daisies and dandelions), 'Taller non-woody plants' (tall grass stalks, buttercups, ferns), 'Small woody plants' (bushes – evergreen and deciduous), 'Tall woody plants' (trees – evergreen and deciduous). These could be dotted around the board as the suggestions come in. The importance at this stage is for the children to recall previous work on habitats and therefore the ordering of the information can follow straight afterwards.

2. Remind the children that scientists always try to order their observations in some way and tell them that they are going to do just that with the information they have gathered about a habitat. Use the example of a woodland habitat and explain how ecologists have used scientific evidence from their studies to divide this type of habitat into four layers – the ground layer (moss), the field layer (buttercups), the shrub layer (bushes) and the tree layer. Write these layers down the side of the board with the ground layer at the bottom.

Independent work
3. Issue the children with pieces of paper and pencils and ask them to copy the names of the layers down the side of the paper.

4. Ask them to use the information about plants from the board and arrange it into layers on their paper. After a few minutes check their answers.

Whole-class work
5. Tell the children that you are now going to consider the animals that live in a habitat. At this point, if children have studied the soil in the past, you may like to say that the soil is a habitat but it also affects the plants that grow in the habitat above it. (The children may wish to discuss work with wormeries or research using secondary sources about moles.)

6. Ask the children about the animals that live in the habitat and point out that they can use the ecologist's idea of layers to help them to order their information.

7. Encourage the children to identify invertebrates (centipedes, millipedes, beetles, snails, slugs and spiders) and vertebrates (shrews, field mice, voles, frogs, lizards and snakes) in the ground layer. They may also identify bees and butterflies visiting flowers in the field layer, with some spiders found in the shrub and tree layer. Birds are the dominant vertebrates in the trees and shrub layer although squirrels may also occur.

■SCHOLASTIC

8. The children may point out that squirrels also visit the ground and this can lead to discussing birds that visit the ground. At this point you could discuss individual bird species (blackbirds, robins and sparrows on the ground and trees, blue and great tits and finches on trees and bushes). You could also use this to say how the use of layers is good for positioning plants in a habitat but it is not as good for animals.

Group/paired work

9. Say that just as scientists bring order to studying a habitat by using layers, they also bring order to the study of living things by having a classification system. Review the children's knowledge of this and look for answers about invertebrates (insects, molluscs, worms), vertebrates (fish, amphibians, reptiles), birds and mammals.

10. The children may also know that plants can be classified as: flowering plants, conifers, ferns, and mosses. Say that classifying living things has lead to the development of keys to help identify them. Issue photocopiable page 36 'Identifying invertebrates' and present the children with a selection of photographs of animals labelled with letters which they must identify using the key. Alternatively, use the interactive activity 'Identifying invertebrates' on the CD-ROM.

Introducing the new area of study

Challenge the children to define 'life cycle' and look for an answer about the stages in the development of a living organism. Ask them about the life cycle of a bird in a local habitat and be prepared for descriptions of birds nesting in roofs, broken eggs, fallen chicks and so on in order to describe the way to a fledged young bird. Ask about the life cycles of any other animals and say that in this half term they are going to find out much more about life cycles including the one they are in – the human life cycle.

Differentiation
• Support children having difficulty in placing the plants in the correct layers by asking them to recall where they saw the plants.
• Challenge children who correctly finish their work early to describe the layers found in a garden or flowerbed.
• Support children by emphasising that they must look closely at the structure of the animal when they are identifying it using a key.
• Challenge children who correctly finish their work early to make a key for the identification of common birds.

Science in the wider world

Ecologists are at work all over the planet studying habitats in order to find out all the plants and animals that live in them, and their ways of life. They also study each habitat over a number of years to find out if the plants and animals in the habitat change or if the habitat itself changes. All this information provides scientific evidence that can be used to support ideas and arguments about climate change.

Review

Ask the children for definitions of the words in the Scientifically speaking section. Move on to ask how ecologists divide up a habitat. Ask the children to describe the habitat they have been studying in the lesson and explain how they can use a key to identify animals in the habitat.

Objectives
● To know that human bodies vary naturally.
● To know that humans have a growth spurt.
● To know that parts of the body change in proportion to growth.

Resources
Graph paper; a children's informal height chart; photocopiable page 37 'Growth'

Speaking scientifically
embryo, foetus, adolescent

Lesson 2: Growth in humans

Introduction
Refer to the habitat in the previous lesson and ask how it changes during a year. Look for an answer about seasons and explain that this is a recurring pattern of events and that living things also follow a pattern in their life cycles as do humans.

Whole-class work
1. Brainstorm the concept of the human life cycle and write ideas on the board. At this stage, consider the life cycle to begin with the development of the baby in the mother's uterus.

2. You may wish to introduce the terms *embryo* and *foetus*. If questions about how the baby is formed arise, say that the life cycle can be taken even further back and that this will be considered later (see week 2, lesson 1).

Independent work
3. On the board, in random order, write: *foetus, infant up to 1 year old, child (from 2–12), adolescent (from 12–18), adult (18 onwards)*.

4. Ask the children to sequence the human life cycle on paper from the information on the board. (Be prepared to talk about death, if the topic arises, but deal with it sensitively.)

Whole-class work
5. Review the life cycle and say that within this pattern there is variation and that the children are now going to investigate it by measuring their heights. Let the children work in pairs to record their heights.

6. Record the data on the board, dividing it into six size groups, and ask the children to construct a bar graph of their results.

7. When complete, discuss how the charts can be used to show the variation in height with small numbers at either end of the range and large numbers in the middle. Say that this is perfectly natural in all populations.

Independent work
8. Issue photocopiable page 37 'Growth' and ask the children to complete it.

Differentiation
● Support children having difficulty constructing graphs.
● Challenge children who have brought in their own measuring charts to produce a line graph from the data.

Science in the wider world
Sound waves beyond our hearing are beamed into the uterus of a pregnant woman and as they bounce harmlessly off the foetus they are used to produce a picture known as a *scan* that can be used to check that the foetus is developing normally.

Review
Ask the children to sequence the stages in the human life cycle. Discuss how variation is natural and identify the growth spurt in boys and girls.

Objectives
● To know about the changes that take place at puberty in males and females.

Resources
Photocopiable page 38 'Changes in the body (1)'; photocopiable page 'Changes in the body (2)' from the CD-ROM; interactive activity 'Changes in the body' on the CD-ROM

Speaking scientifically
puberty, hormones, penis, scrotum, testicles, ovaries, vulva

Lesson 3: Changes in the body

Introduction
Remind the children of the human life cycle that they constructed in the last lesson and how the shape of the body changes. Remind them also about the growth spurt which occurs in childhood and which many may be going through at the moment. Say that in this lesson they are going to look at how the body changes in the first part of adolescence – a period of time called 'puberty'.

Whole-class work
1. Talk about the outward differences between adult males and females – broader male shoulders, broader female hips and so on.

2. Talk about the differences between the male and the female reproductive systems, explaining that most of the male system is on the outside of the body and that almost all the female reproductive system is inside her body except for the vulva.

3. Remind the children of their study of the skeleton earlier in their science course and say that both males and females have hip bones and that one of the bones at the front is called the pubis and during puberty hairs grow in the skin around it in both males and females. This is where the word *puberty* comes from.

4. Talk about the changes that take place at puberty: hair grows in the armpits, males hair starts to grow on the face, body shape and features change, male voices 'break', the skin of both sexes produces more oil and this can lead to the formation of spots. Explain that all these changes are produced by chemicals called hormones.

Independent work
5. Give each child photocopiable page 38 'Changes in the body (1)' and let them work through it.

> ### Differentiation
> ● Support children in completing the photocopiable sheet by reading through the text.
> ● Challenge children by giving them photocopiable page 'Changes in the body (2)' from the CD-ROM and let them complete it.

Science in the wider world
Special creams have been developed to help treat spots during puberty. Sanitary towels have been developed for absorbing blood produced when a period occurs.

Review
Use the interactive activity 'Changes in the body' on the CD-ROM to go through the earlier discussion and make sure the children know the terms that have been introduced.

Objectives
● To know about the structure and function of the male and female reproductive systems.

Resources
Photocopiable page 'Female reproductive system' from the CD-ROM; photocopiable page 'Male reproductive system' from the CD-ROM; photocopiable page 39 'The reproductive system (1)'; photocopiable page 40 'The reproductive system (2)'; 'The reproductive system' on the CD-ROM

Speaking scientifically
ovum, sperm, nucleus, DNA, zygote

Lesson 1: The reproductive systems

Introduction
Say that in this lesson the children are going to study the structure and function of the male and female reproductive organs.

Whole-class work
1. Display photocopiable page 'Female reproductive system' from the CD-ROM. Talk about each part in turn and, as you mention it, write its name on the board.

2. Leave the section on the egg cell for the moment and display photocopiable page 'Male reproductive system' from the CD-ROM and do the same.

3. Having introduced the names of the human reproductive system, revise them by pointing to each part on the diagrams and asking the children to call out the names from the words on the board.

4. Once the class is familiar with the names, return to looking at the diagram of the female reproductive system and talk about the path the sperms travel and fertilisation.

5. Now look at the egg cell and point out the nucleus. Say that the word *information* in the label refers to DNA. Say that the head of the sperm also contains a nucleus with DNA from the male and that it is the joining together of the DNA from both sexes that provides the complete instructions for the growth and development of the new individual.

Independent work
6. Give children photocopiable page 39 'The reproductive system (1)' and 'The reproductive system (2)' on page 40 and let them complete them. You can also use interactive activity 'The reproductive system' on the CD-ROM.

Differentiation
● Support children in completing the photocopiable sheet by allowing them to work in pairs.
● Challenge children to find out more about DNA.

Science in the wider world
The DNA of every person is unique and so it can be used to identify people. DNA can be extracted from organic remains such as blood and saliva left at crime scenes and used to catch criminals.

Review
Go through the children's work with them making sure they know the names of the structures of the reproductive systems and the functions.

Objectives
● To know about the development of the baby in the uterus.

Resources
Photocopiable page 'Life before birth' from the CD-ROM; rulers and paper; scissors; glue; modelling clay – individual lumps about 6cm in diameter; you may also wish to organise a visit from a midwife

Speaking scientifically
placenta, pregnant

Lesson 2: Life before birth

Introduction
Remind the children of the structure of the human egg. Ask them what happens when an egg and sperm meet.

Independent work
1. Tell the children they are going to piece together the story of what happens to the fertilised egg and give each child photocopiable page 'Life before birth' from the CD-ROM.

2. Tell them to cut out the pictures and boxes of text, match them together, arrange them in order and stick them down on a piece of A4 paper.

Group work
3. Let the children in each group check each other's work and circulate and check them too.

4. Ask the children to use the information in the sequence to draw life-size pictures of the developing baby. These should then be coloured and arranged in order to form a display.

Whole-class work
5. Tell the children that pregnant women are sometimes described as *eating for two*. Using their knowledge of digestion and the body, challenge the children to think how the food could get to the baby. Do not expect an accurate reply, but look for creative ideas based on rudimentary science knowledge. Conclude by saying that the mother digests the food and it travels in her blood to the uterus where it comes into contact with the surface of the placenta. This is a structure produced by the embryo to hold on to the wall of the uterus.

6. Challenge them to think how the baby gets its oxygen and steer them towards the idea that the oxygen is taken into the mother's blood in her lungs, travels to the placenta and goes across into the baby's blood. Ask what might happen to the carbon dioxide the baby produces and steer them towards saying it passes across the placenta to the mother's blood and is exhaled in her breath.

Differentiation
● Support children having difficulties constructing life-size pictures by helping them draw a line then 'flesh out' the illustration on either side of the line.
● Challenge children to produce a scale model of the 39-week foetus using modelling clay. The model could be ten times smaller, having a length of 5.2cm.

Science in the wider world
The scientific study of childbirth has contributed greatly to the practice of midwifery in the safe delivery of babies. Premature babies, that in earlier times would have died, are kept alive by placing them in incubators. Incubators keep the babies warm and supply other needs such as food and oxygen to help them develop and gain weight.

Review
Take a ball of modelling clay and say it represents a zygote then divide it into two, then four and then eight pieces, keeping them together to say that an embryo is forming. Ask the children to describe what happens next.

Objectives
● To understand the difference between a life cycle and a timeline.
● To know and recognise the stages in the human timeline.

Resources
Collections of photographs cut from magazines showing two or three of: infants, children, adolescents, young adults, older adults (with families) middle-aged people, people in old age; scissors; card; glue

Speaking scientifically
infant, adolescent, hormones, weaned, stabiliser, menopause, life style

Lesson 3: The human timeline

Introduction

Review the human life cycle from page 16. Say that this focuses on stages related to growth and reproduction. Say that in this lesson they are going to look at all the stages in a human life and construct and use a human timeline.

Whole-class work

1. Create a human timeline on the board with the children, using the following sequence: infant up to 1 year; child 1–12 years; adolescent 12–18 years; young adult 18–21 years; adult 21–55 years; middle age 55–65; old age 65+ years.)

2. Comment on the stages as follows:
● The infant is fed on milk until the age of six months, then on milk and special baby food for the rest of infancy and into childhood until the age of about two. From then on, the child can eat a normal diet and is said to be weaned. Cows' milk should continue to be part of the diet.
● The child grows steadily and learns to sit up, stand, walk, use a cup and spoon and moves onto reading, swimming and riding a bicycle.
● During adolescence (12–18 years) the body produces hormones which develop the sex organs and prepare it for reproduction (see page 17).
● The adult stage begins at 18 but sometimes an early span of 18–21 years is used to describe this stage. People establish a way of life for themselves.
● In the adult stage from 21–55, people may form partnerships and have children (and even grandchildren). It is a time of further career development and establishment in the community. From 45–55, a woman's sex hormones decrease during the menopause; the woman can no longer have babies.
● Middle age is considered to be from 55–65. The body shows signs of ageing, such as wrinkles, and there is a tendency to put on weight. Muscles are no longer as strong as they were but exercise can help to stay fit.
● Old age is considered to be 65 but many people of that age consider it to begin at 70+. Further wrinkling, weight changes and loss of strength continues. Injuries take longer to heal and bones become more fragile and liable to break. Various body organs may work less well leading to an increase in health care. The brain, for example, may perform its memory function less well (mental exercises can improve this). With a healthy life style, it is possible to remain active and alert well into old age of 85+.

Independent, group or paired work

3. Ask the children to arrange the photographs of people from magazines into stages on a human timeline.

> **Differentiation**
> ● Support children in their organisation of the pictures and the captions.
> ● Challenge children to place people in their family and neighbourhood into various stages of the human timeline. They could plot a bar graph of the numbers in each stage.

Science in the wider world

Improved diet and health care has improved infancy survival rates in many countries. As technologies are developed to help people remain well and independent, more people live well into old age.

Review

Ask the children to name the stages on the time line and challenge them to place the school staff, regular visitors and volunteers along its various stages.

Objectives
● To learn about the life cycles of mammals.
● To research and present information about the three kinds of mammals.

Resources
Internet access

Speaking scientifically
mammal, gestation period, weaning, placenta, marsupial, x–axis, y–axis

Lesson 1: Life cycle: a mammal

Introduction
Ask the children what 'mammal' means. Look for answers about having skin covered by fur and mothers providing milk for their young. Consider how humans can be classified as mammals. Ask about other mammals that might share their home. Ask which mammals might live on a farm and in a zoo.

Independent work
1. Remind the children how long it takes for a human baby to develop (39 weeks or 273 days). Explain that in other mammals this is the *gestation period*.

2. Write these gestation periods on the board: rabbit 32 days, rat 21 days, hamster 16 days, fox 53 days, guinea pig 68 days, sheep 148 days. Ask the children to arrange them in animal size order and make a bar graph of the data.

3. Ask them to identify a result that does not fit the pattern and offer an explanation. (It's the guinea pig; when it is born it is able to run around and feed almost straightaway – it is better developed.)

Whole-class work
4. Explain that, as humans are weaned onto solid food by about two years old, each species of mammal is also weaned over a certain time.

5. Say that some species such as rabbits have large litters several times a year while others such as foxes have a smaller litter once a year.

6. Tell the children that in some mammal species, such as deer, the males grow antlers and spend time displaying and fighting to gain a mate.

7. Point out that all the mammals the class have studied so far are placental mammals – the embryos are connected by a circular structure called a placenta to the uterus wall for the whole of its development. Say that there are two other kinds of mammals: marsupials (which rear an early-stage embryo in a pouch) and egg-laying mammals.

Independent, group or paired work
8. Ask the children to find out about the life cycles of a few placental mammals and the life cycle of a marsupial and an egg-laying mammal.

9. Invite the children to create a poster that compares the similarities differences they discovered in their research.

> **Differentiation**
> ● Support children making the bar graph and the line graph.
> ● Challenge the children to describe the growth of the hamster. Elicit that it initially grows quickly (up to nine days), then slower (to 35 days) then much more slowly (to 84 days).

Science in the wider world
Scientists study the breeding behaviour of endangered mammals in natural habitats and use discoveries to set up breeding programmes in zoos.

Review
Ask the children to present their research into the life cycles of mammals to the class, displaying their knowledge of gestation period, weaning and growth.

Objectives
● To learn about the life cycle of a bird.
● To find out about the risks to survival during the life cycle.

Resources
Bird song (for example, from the RSPB website) audio; media resource 'Parts of the egg' on the CD-ROM; photocopiable page 'Song thrush survival game' from the CD-ROM; an unfertilised hen's egg(s) broken into a saucer (with the egg shell present, one piece showing the air space); video clip of a chick hatching (sourced from the internet)

Speaking scientifically
moult, clutch, incubation, brood

Lesson 2: Life cycle: a bird

Introduction
Say that birds are some of the most frequently seen animals in the local environment. Take the children outside to look for and identify some. Say that at this time of year the young birds are establishing themselves as adults and that adults are completing their moult ready for the winter.

Whole-class work
1. Back in the classroom, tell the children that you are going to rewind back to the springtime when the bird life cycle begins. If the children studied mammals in the previous lesson remind them of those that displayed to attract a mate. Say that all male birds put on a display which involves singing. Play some birds songs from a website. Say that once a pair has mated they build a nest and the female lays a clutch of eggs in it over several days.

Independent work
2. Show the children media resource 'Parts of the egg' on the CD-ROM and go through the labels together.

3. Show the broken egg. Ask them to identify the parts and draw a labelled diagram of it.

Whole-class work
4. Say that after the last egg has been laid the incubation process begins with one or both parents, in turn, sitting on the eggs to keep them warm. In a fertilised egg, a disc of tissue forms on the yolk and uses the food stored in it to form the chick. When this process is complete the chick bursts into the air space and then chips its way out of the shell. Show a film of a chick hatching.

5. Say that after the chick hatches out it is known as a nestling and is fed by its parents. During this time it grows and acquires a full complement of feathers, learns to flap its wings and leaves the nest. It is now known as a fledgling. It continues to practise its flying skills and is fed by the parents. Eventually the young bird learns how to find its own food and is no longer fed or cared for by the parent. When this happens the fledgling stage has passed.

Group work
6. Explain that once an egg is laid it does not guarantee that the chick will hatch and grow to be an adult.

7. Give each group of three children photocopiable page 'Song thrush survival game' from the CD-ROM. Say that the song thrush usually attempts to raise three broods (or families) and each group member will be responsible for the fate of a brood. Go through the sheet with the children then let them play the game and see which brood has the greatest number of survivors.

Differentiation
● Support children in identifying the parts of the open egg and advise them on making an accurate drawing. Check that label lines reach the correct places on the drawing.
● Challenge children to add the annotation from the diagram of the egg to the labels of their drawing.

Science in the wider world
Many birds are endangered due to a variety of factors. Institutions such as the RSPB and the British Trust for Ornithology conduct research and gather data on birds to assess their changing populations.

Review
Ask the children to produce a life cycle of a bird – egg, nestling, young bird (including fledgling), adult. For each stage in the life cycle encourage the children to identify risks to survival.

Objectives
- To learn about the life cycle of a frog.
- To learn about the different kinds of amphibians.

Resources
Photocopiable sheet 'The life cycle of a frog' on CD-ROM; large sheets of paper; scissors; glue; secondary sources on amphibians and the midwife toad

Speaking scientifically
amphibian, external, internal gill, metamorphosis

Lesson 3: Life cycle: amphibians

Introduction
Ask the children what they understand by the word amphibian. Look for answers including living in water and on land or specific animals such as frog, newt or toad. Say that all these answers are correct and that a member of the amphibian group begins its life cycle in water and develops into an adult that can survive on land.

Independent or paired work
1. Ask the children about the young stage of an amphibian and look for an answer about a tadpole. Ask the children to describe a tadpole (it is black and has a tail. Some children who have reared tadpoles may mention the presence of legs. Tell the children that to sort out the information about tadpoles they are to look at the stages of the development of a frog.

2. Give out the photocopiable page 'The life cycle of a frog' from the CD-ROM and ask them to draw a picture for each caption. Say that the pictures and their captions are mixed up on the page. Challenge the children to cut them out to rearrange them into the correct sequence. Invite the children to mount their life cycles on a large sheet of paper in the form of a life cycle.

Whole-class work
3. Let the children display their life cycles and check them. Say that this complete change of form from a fish-like animal to a frog is called metamorphosis.

Independent or paired work
4. Challenge the children to use secondary sources to investigate these statements:
- All frogs live on the ground.
- The spawn of frogs, toads and newts look the same.
- All amphibians have four legs.
- All tadpoles develop in ponds.

Differentiation
- Support children to look closely at the pictures and help them arrange them in order.
- Challenge children to find out what is unusual about the midwife toad.

Science in the wider world
The populations of some species of amphibians have greatly reduced in some countries due to various factors including loss of habitat. Laws have been passed to protect them, making it illegal to kill them, keep them as pets or damage their remaining habitats.

Review
Challenge the children to imagine they are a newly-hatched tadpole. Ask them to describe the changes they go through as they become frogs.

Let the children present their reports on amphibians. They should include these facts:
- some frogs live in trees
- frog spawn forms a bunch, toad spawn is laid in lines and newt spawn is laid singly under leaves
- there is a group of amphibians called caecilians which do not have legs
- tadpoles of tree frogs can develop in pools of water in a plant.

Objectives
• To learn about the life cycle of the butterfly.
• To learn that some insects have nymph stages instead of caterpillar stages.

Resources
X-ray photograph of a limb showing the bones (on the internet); 'cardboard armour': a large cardboard box with cut-out holes for the head and arms, strips of cardboard to wrap around the arms and legs, sticky tape to hold the cardboard around the limbs, a smaller cardboard box open at one lower end with eye nose, mouth holes in it to make a 'helmet'; scissors; secondary sources on the life cycle of a grass hopper or locust; internet access

Speaking scientifically
vertebrate, invertebrate, endoskeleton, exoskeleton, moulting, instar, nymph

Lesson 1: Life cycle: an insect

Introduction
Say that birds belong to a group called vertebrates. Ask what the word means. Draw animals with back bones. Say that mammals and amphibians belong to this group. Explain that there is another group called invertebrates. Ask what this might mean. Look for an answer about animals without a backbone. Take the children outside to find invertebrates. Steer them to look for insect life.

Whole-class work
1. In the classroom, remind the children that vertebrates have a skeleton inside their bodies. Show them the X-ray. Say that internal skeletons are endoskeletons.

2. Draw the outline of an insect limb on the board. Say when it is X-rayed it looks the same because no bones are inside; on the outside are thick plates of armour to which the muscles attach. The armour is an outside skeleton (exoskeleton). Draw some thick lines on the outside of the limb to show this.

3. Ask the children what they would look like if they had exoskeletons. Ask for a volunteer to put on the cardboard armour. Remind the children that as they grow their bones grow too. Say that the exoskeleton does not grow, yet insects like caterpillars increase in size. Ask for suggestions for how they do it. Encourage a wide range of suggestions; don't dismiss the fanciful ones.

4. Explain that when an insect is ready to increase in size its body pushes on the exoskeleton and makes it split and fall away (moulting). Underneath is a softer armour which can stretch but hardens as it is exposed to the air. Ask: *How might the insect underneath stretch its skin before it grows?* From the answers, explain that the insect takes in air and blows itself up; in time it grows new flesh underneath to fill the air spaces.

Independent work
5. Ask the children to describe the life cycle of a butterfly, comprising the four main stages (egg; caterpillar or larva; chrysalis of pupa; adult). Draw a simple life cycle on the board with the stages labelled. Say that there is one stage when the animal is feeding and growing and ask the children to identify it (the caterpillar). Ask how accurate this diagram is, given that they know a tiny caterpillar must come out of an egg and a large caterpillar turns into a pupa. Elicit answers about the caterpillar increasing in size as it grows.

6. Explain that each stage of an insect's growth is called an *instar*. The first instar is the one that leaves the egg. Ask the children to research the typical length of each instar of a caterpillar. They can record them in a table and produce a bar graph of caterpillar growth.

Independent or paired work
7. Explain that some insects (grasshopper and locust) have a different life cycle to the butterfly. Ask them to discover what it is (nymph stage not caterpillar).

Differentiation
• Support children taking the measurements and creating the bar graph.
• Challenge children to produce a line graph of the results. They should draw a line as if the bars were next to each other and the line ran along their tops and up their side.

Science in the wider world
Blowflies have a similar life cycle to butterflies and their maggots live in dead bodies. Forensic scientists investigate the blow fly maggots and pupa in a decaying corpse to find out how long it has been dead.

Review
Ask the children to compare the life cycles of a butterfly and a grasshopper.

Objectives
● To learn about the life cycle of a tree frog.
● To learn about the life cycles of other rainforest animals.

Resources
A bromeliad with a water-filled centre; media resource 'Tree frog' on the CD-ROM; safety glasses; a plastic cup; an elastic band that can stretch around it; tape measure or metre rule; a quiet place; clean plastic bottles; secondary sources on rainforest animals

Speaking scientifically
tree frog, resonator

Lesson 2: Rainforest animals

Introduction
Ask the children what they already know about the rainforest. Talk about the different layers and explain that animals are found in every layer, working through their life cycles.

Whole-class work
1. Say that one of the most numerous animals found in the dark lower layers of the rainforest is the tree frog. Ask the children to describe the life cycle of the frog.

2. Say that in the rainforest there are not many ponds but the rain falls frequently and can be caught by plants. Ask how this might help the frogs and look for an answer about pools developing on the plants.

3. Show the class a bromeliad with a water-filled centre and say that the plant grows on the branch of a tree.

Paired work
4. Look at the media resource 'Tree frog' on the CD-ROM and point out the swelling under its chin. Say that this is a resonator and male frogs use it to tell females that they are present. Ask children why frogs need to make a loud noise. (It's difficult to see in the dark lower layer of the rainforest.)

5. Tell the children that they are going to plan an investigation to find out if the resonator allows sound to be heard at a greater distance.

6. Using an elastic band to model the vocal cords and a plastic cup as a resonator, the children should record the distances and write up the investigation. The children must keep the stretched bands away from their eyes. They should conclude that the resonator allows sounds to be heard over a greater distance.

Independent work
7. Ask the children to use secondary sources to find out about the life cycles of one or more rainforest animals. They should present their findings and include the headings: *Born or hatched?* and *Raising the young.*

> ### Differentiation
> ● Support children, through careful pairing, in measuring distances and in listening carefully.
> ● Challenge children to see if an empty plastic bottle can be used as a resonator by blowing over it and ask them to compare its effect with simply blowing through the lips.

Science in the wider world
Rainforests are under threat from mining operations, timber collecting and clearing for fields and towns. Scientists study the life cycles of rainforest animals to find out how the effects of humans are affecting them and the information is used to plan conservation schemes.

Review
Let the children present the results of their investigations about resonators and assess their importance in the life cycle of the frog in bringing the males and females together in the rainforest gloom. The children should then report their researches into the various rainforest animals they have studied.

Objectives
● To know the zones of the ocean.
● To know the life cycle of a marine creature.

Resources
A globe; items collected from the seashore (shells, dogfish and whelk egg cases and so on) in a transparent box; photocopiable page 41 'The life cycle of the silver eel'; scissors; photocopiable page 'Map of the world' from the CD-ROM; atlases; large pieces of card; glue; secondary sources about marine life

Speaking scientifically
polar regions, incubate, strand line, marine

Lesson 3: Animals in the ocean

Introduction
Use a globe to show the children the extent of the oceans on the planet (two thirds of the surface). Ask them to name the oceans and point to each one in turn. Talk about evidence we can find of animals that live in the sea and look at the objects from the seashore.

Whole-class work
1. Remind the children how ecologists divide woodlands and rainforests into layers and say that ecologists divide up the oceans into five zones (the sunlight zone, the twilight zone, the midnight zone, the abyss and the trenches).

2. Say that coral reefs are in the sunlight zone and are permanently covered with warm seawater. Explain that coral reefs are known for the diversity of their living things, but life is found at all levels in the sea.

Independent/paired work
3. Issue photocopiable page 41 'The life cycle of the silver eel' and ask the children to cut out and arrange the pictures in order.

4. Give the children atlases and ask them to find the area of the Atlantic called the Sargasso Sea where the eels go to breed and mark it on photocopiable page 'Map of the world' from the CD-ROM.

5. Tell the children to stick the map to a larger card and arrange the life cycle from the egg in the Sargasso Sea to the silver eel coming halfway back towards the Sargasso Sea. They should draw in arrows showing the path of the eels to Europe and back to the Sargasso Sea.

6. Ask the children how the eel changes during its life cycle.

7. Talk about how the eel completes its life cycle in the sunlight zone and tell the children to find out, and write about, a marine creature that lives in another zone.

Differentiation
● Support children by helping them with the sequencing and mapping of the eel.
● Challenge some children to find more animals that live in different zones of the oceans.

Science in the wider world
Marine ecologists measure the sizes of populations of marine animals to find out if they are being affected by the activity of humans.

Review
Let the children describe the lives of the marine creatures they have researched and compare them with the eel.

Objectives
● To learn about the life cycles of desert animals.

Resources
A globe; photocopiable page 42 'The desert tortoise'; ruler; a ball of modelling clay about 12cm in diameter for each pair; secondary sources about deserts

Speaking scientifically
desert, hibernate, incubate, prey

Lesson 1: Animals in the desert

Introduction
Look at the globe and point out the main desert regions. Say that each desert has its own wild creatures that the children will study, but that you are going to begin by looking at the North American Desert and the desert tortoise.

Whole-class work
1. Read together the account on photocopiable page 42 'The desert tortoise'.

2. Read the account again, slowly, and ask the children to make some notes to help them prepare a display about the life cycle of the tortoise using modelling clay and text.

Individual work
3. Using their notes to help them, let the children make their models to scale and put relevant text next to each one.

4. Let the children use secondary sources about deserts to find out about the life cycles of other animals that live in other deserts and the average life spans of a range of mammals of their own choosing.

Differentiation
● Support children in their calculation work and scaling to prepare measurements for their models.
● Challenge children to describe the lives (including life cycles) of one animal from each of the deserts featured in the introduction.

Science in the wider world
Ecologists study the life cycles of many desert animals in detail to help in conservation work, as a variation in the extreme conditions in which they live can sometimes threaten the survival of one or more species.

Review
Ask the children to display their models and describe the life cycles of the animals they have researched.

Objectives
● To learn about the life cycles of dinosaurs.
● To understand how the activities of living animals can help to explain the fossil evidence of extinct ones.

Resources
A space which can accommodate 65 strides, such as the hall; rolls of wallpaper; sticky tape; graph paper; photocopiable page 'Dinosaur growth' from the CD-ROM

Speaking scientifically
mammoth, reptile

Lesson 2: Dinosaur lives

Introduction

Review any work that the children have done on fossils in Year 3 and evolution and fossil evidence in Year 4. Then say that you are going to construct a human timeline about fossil evidence. Take the children out into the playground and pick one child to stand still and represent the present day. Say that each stride represents a million years and, in turn, get other children to take the following number of strides away from the present day: two strides to represent the first humans; five strides for mammoths; ten strides for giant camels; 20 strides for the first apes; 30 strides for humming birds; 40 strides for whales; 50 strides for horses; 60 strides for penguins; 65 strides for dinosaurs.

Group/paired work

1. Tell the children that dinosaurs belonged to the reptile group, like the desert tortoise, and that both were living at the same time. Say that scientists sometimes use the behaviour of living animals to tell them about extinct ones. Ask what the lives of tortoises may tell us about the lives of dinosaurs (males fighting, making nests, egg laying, no parental care).

2. Pretend that fossil nests of a dinosaur called maiasaura have been found. In the hall, ask the children to cut a strip of paper 120cm long by 8cm wide. They should make it into a circle and secure with sticky tape for the outline of a nest. The children should then cut out 15 paper circles 8cm in diameter for the eggs and put them in the nest. (This nest is about half the actual size.)

3. Set up another dinosaur nest site (again half the actual size) placing it 3m from the other one. Ask: *Why did the dinosaurs build their nests together?* (A better chance of some eggs surviving a predator attack.) *Why were they so far apart?* (The mothers could get round them and look after them.) *How does the fossil evidence of Maiasaura suggests that the dinosaur behaved differently to the tortoise?* (It looked after the eggs.)

Independent work

4. Tell the children that dinosaur bones have growth rings like trees and by using them, and by looking at the size of the bones, scientists can work out how some dinosaurs grew.

5. Issue photocopiable page 'Dinosaur growth' from the CD-ROM and ask the children to complete it.

> **Differentiation**
> ● Support children to make a table for the data, choosing axes for the graph and plotting the points.
> ● Challenge children to find out about dinosaur tracks and draw how they think the tracks would look of an animal walking around the nests.

Science in the wider world

The study of fossil bones and trace fossils (evidence of activity such as nest building and footprints) helps to build a picture of the past that can be used to explain how life evolved.

Review

Discuss how fossils provide evidence about the life cycles of dinosaurs.

Objectives
- To learn about the life of Sir David Attenborough.
- To learn about a favourite animal.

Resources
Secondary sources about animals; access to the internet

Speaking scientifically
natural history, naturalist, zoology, geology

Lesson 3: Sir David Attenborough

Introduction
Tell the class they are going to look at the life of a famous film-maker called Sir David Attenborough. Ask them if they have seen any of his programmes on television and talk about any programmes the children may have seen. Ask: *What are his films generally about?* (plants and animals)

Whole-class work
1. Explain that when Sir David Attenborough was a boy, he became interested in the natural world and collected stones, fossils and other natural history objects. Talk about any things that the children collect. Focus on those that have a natural history theme, such as shells. Ask what other natural-history objects naturalists might collect and look for answers about feathers and bones.

2. Talk about how David is a very successful TV presenter and talk about the things that you need to do to be a good presenter. Ask: *Why do you think David might be such a good presenter?* (He's very interested in natural history.)

Group/paired work
3. Tell the children that they are going to write about a favourite animal as if they were going to talk about it on a TV documentary.

4. Tell them to find out about the animal's structure, habitat, life cycle and so on, and then write a vivid description about it. Encourage them to think carefully about the how to make their pieces both interesting and informative.

5. Children can present their pieces as if they were presenting a TV documentary. They can rehearse their presentation ready for the review.

Differentiation
- Support children by helping them select animals that can be easily researched.
- Challenge children to find photographs and use other props to support their presentations.

Science in the wider world
Natural history broadcasting aims to generate interest in the natural world and motivate people to conserve plants and animals around the world.

Review
Let the children present their work and discuss how they generated interest. Keep comments positive.

Objectives
• To learn about the effect of camouflage.

Resources
Media resource 'Banded snails' on the CD-ROM; each group will need enough modelling clay to make 20 balls with a 2cm diameter; a selection of paints; paint brushes; stopwatch

Speaking scientifically
camouflage, silicon

Lesson 1: Sir David Attenborough and camouflage

Introduction
Tell the children that one of Sir David Attenborough's first programmes was about camouflage. Ask the children what the word means and why animals might need to use camouflage.

Whole-class work
1. Say that one common animal that is found in many habitats, including gardens, is the banded snail. Show the children the media resource 'Banded snails' on the CD-ROM. Ask: *Why do the shells vary in colour?*

2. Say that the snails are the prey of birds, and ask how you could investigate which of these patterns could help best with camouflage.

3. Discuss how scientists sometimes use models in their investigations and ask how models could be used in this one.

Group/paired work
4. Let the children plan an investigation using the school grounds in which to test their models. A workable plan would be to make 20 model shells of the same colour and paint half of them with five bands. One child places them at random in long green grass and another child, looking down on the area as a bird would in flight, is then given a minute to find as many as they can. This should be repeated with the same person putting them out but with different people acting as *birds*. The number of each type collected by each 'bird' should be recorded.

5. Ask the children how they could see if they get the same results in other parts of the habitat and look for an answer featuring short grass and long yellow grass. Say that sometimes the snails are found in bushes and let the children design and carry out an investigation to see how the snails are camouflaged there.

6. Let the children present their results using bar graphs of un-banded and banded snails for each location.

Independent work
7. When the investigation is complete, ask the children to write a report of it as if they were going to read it out like Sir David Attenborough in one of his programmes.

8. Check their work and select the most realistic to read out in the review.

> **Differentiation**
> • Support children in making models the same size and in organising their activities in the investigation.
> • Challenge children to make ten models with eight bands and test them against the five-banded snails.

Science in the wider world
Ecologists study populations of animals to find out what they eat and what preys on them. From this they can work out how the animal fits into the food chain.

Review
Let the children present their results and conclusions to the class. The results will depend on the surroundings, but they may find that the models of snails without bands are less visible and therefore less frequently picked up in green grass while banded models are less frequently picked up in brown grass.

Objectives
● To learn about the life of Jane Goodall.

Resources
Photocopiable page 43 'Dame Jane Goodall'

Speaking scientifically
tool

Lesson 2: Jane Goodall and animal behaviour

Introduction

Ask the children if they had a cuddly toy when they were younger. Ask: *What kind was it? What was its name?* Tell the children that the lesson today is about a scientist who had a toy chimp called Jubilee. Her name is Jane Goodall and she was born in 1934.

Whole-class work

1. Give out copies of photocopiable page 43 'Dame Jane Goodall' and read through the information on Jane's childhood together (the first paragraph). Ask: *Were you fascinated by animals when you were young? Have you ever been inspired by a book?*

2. Talk about the club Jane started and let the children work on their own for a few moments to see if they could have passed the test to join Jane's club.

3. Read the paragraph that explains how Jane moved to Kenya and began her research into the behaviour of chimpanzees. Remind children that scientists often study the behaviour of living animals to find out about animals that are extinct.

Independent work

4. Remind the children that so far in studying animals they have only looked at their bodies and where they live. Explain how observations on their behaviour, like Jane made on the chimpanzees, can lead to important discoveries.

5. Ask the children to write about an animal's behaviour. They can write about their pets, or any animals they have watched either in their habitat (such as garden birds) or on film.

> ### Differentiation
> ● Support children in recalling the behaviour of their pets or observations on other animals.
> ● Challenge children to write their account using names for animals, then go back over the account and write a number for each animal as scientists used to do before Jane began using names.

Science in the wider world

Many scientists study animal behaviour in their habitats in order to try and build up a complete account of the animal's way of life. This information is used in conservation work.

Review

Ask some children to read out their accounts using names and some children to read out their accounts using numbers. Discuss the advantages and disadvantages of each method.

Objectives
● To learn about the work of Dame Jane Goodall at Gombe National Park.
● To learn about the Jane Goodall Institute.

Resources
Access to the internet; bird feeders; bird food; notebook; books on bird identification

Speaking scientifically
ethologist, botany, monitor

Lesson 3: The work of Jane Goodall

Introduction

Ask the children what they can remember about Jane Goodall from the last lesson. Ask them to use the internet to find the location of the Gombe Nature Reserve. Say that the children are now going to find out about chimpanzees themselves.

Independent work

1. Ask children to spend some time finding out about one aspect of the chimpanzee's behaviour – nest building. Ask them to write down their observations and when they have finished, let some children read their descriptions of nesting behaviour to the class.

Whole-class work

2. Tell children that the work of the Gombe Stream Research Centre on chimpanzee behaviour continues today, but other species are now also studied.

3. The Jane Goodall Institute for Wildlife Research also has an organisation for young people called *Roots and Shoots*.

4. Ask the children to use the internet to find out about the research carried out at these two organisations.

Group/paired work

5. Ask the groups to think of a project that they could do in their locality in order to show their care for animals or the environment. Encourage the children to think about birds in particular.

6. Ask them to think about how they could bring more birds into the school grounds (set up a feeding station). Ask them to produce a plan for that.

7. Discuss their plans and select a site for a feeding station that can be easily seen from the classroom window.

8. Set up a 'research station' by the window with a logbook and books on bird identification and make regular observations from it for few days before the feeding station is installed. After installation, continue to observe and record data for a few days. (The activity could be extended by testing different foods to find out about their impact on bird numbers.)

Differentiation
● Support children to develop ideas and write them down in an orderly way.
● Challenge children to identify the birds without the use of reference books. Ask them to write a description of each type of bird that could be used instead of a picture for identification.

Science in the wider world

Research stations are set up all over the world. Scientists live and work in these stations collecting data about plant and animal life and weather conditions. A lot of this data is used in studies on climate change.

Review

Remind the children of how Jane's toy chimpanzee has lead to the worldwide work she does today and that her work has been an inspiration to others to follow in caring for the planet.

Objectives
● To describe the life cycle of humans.

Resources
Photocopiable page 'Female reproductive system'; photocopiable 'Male reproductive system'; photocopiable page 'Test of reproduction in humans' all from the CD-ROM

Working scientifically
● Reporting and presenting findings from enquiries in written forms.

The human life cycle

Revise
● Revise the key words from the children's work on reproduction. Revise the diagrams showing the human reproductive organs on photocopiable page 'Female reproductive system' and photocopiable page 'Male reproductive system'.

Assess
● Give out photocopiable page 'Test of reproduction in humans' from the CD-ROM and ask the children to complete the test.
● The answers are:
  ● Title: male reproductive system; female reproductive system
  ● I prostate gland; 2 sperm tube; 3 testes or testicle; 4 scrotum; 5 penis
  ● I oviduct (fallopian tube); 2 ovary; 3 uterus (womb); 4 cervix; 5 vagina
  ● The sperm should have a nucleus in the head and the egg should have a nucleus near its centre.
  ● DNA
  ● sperm tube; penis; vagina; cervix; uterus; oviduct
  ● fertilisation (conception)
  ● zygote; embryo; foetus; baby; infant; adolescent; adult

Further practice
● Any further development of the basic features presented in this book should be made following school procedures and with sensitivity. It may be better just to stay with the basic facts presented here and simply go through them again.

Objectives
● To explain the differences in the life cycles of a mammal, an amphibian, an insect and a bird.

Resources
All of the work the children have done on animal life cycles. They could also have access to the library books they used in their researches.

Working scientifically
● Reporting and presenting findings from enquiries in written forms.
● Note: the purpose of this activity is for the children to use their research to answer general questions about the four types of animal, in readiness for the third assessment in which they use their knowledge and research to make the more difficult skills involved in making comparisons in their explanations.

Life cycles of animals

Revise
● Revise the words relevant to animal life cycles and in particular these words: *invertebrate, vertebrate, gestation period, life span, endangered, incubate, hibernate.*
● Let the children use their written work and secondary sources to review the work they have done on animal life cycles. Say that in the assessment they will be asked ten general questions on life cycles and then they will be asked to write an account of the life cycle of any animal they choose so they should research one animal thoroughly for that answer.

Assess
● Read out the following questions and ask the children to write down their answers.
  ● What is the life cycle of an organism?
  ● What is the life span of an organism?
  ● Name four animals that have gestation periods. (for example, cow, horse sheep, mouse).
  ● To which vertebrate group do these animals belong? (mammals)
  ● In which animal group do the mothers provide milk for the young? (mammals)
  ● Name four animals that incubate the early stages of their young? (for example, duck, hen, sparrow, eagle)
  ● To which vertebrate group do these animals belong? (birds)
  ● Name two animals that undergo metamorphose as they grow up. (frog, butterfly, eel)
  ● What does migration mean?
  ● Name an animal that migrates during its life cycle. (eel, barnacle goose)
● Now ask them to write about the life cycle of an animal they have studied.

Further practice
● The children could use the headings: hatching/birth, incubation/providing milk, parental care/no parental care, steady growth/metamorphosis, resident/migrant, short life span (under five years)/long life span (over five years) to research and then describe the life cycles of animals they have not previously studied.

Objectives
● To explain the differences in the life cycles of a mammal, an amphibian, an insect and a bird.

Resources
All of the work the children have done on animal life cycles; interactive activity 'Life cycles' on the CD-ROM

Working scientifically
● Reporting and presenting findings including explanations of results in written forms such as displays or other presentations.
● Note the purpose of this activity is to test the children's ability in making comparisons using such phrases as *similar to* and *different from*. It further tests their comprehension by the way they can translate one form of information into another – the merging of information from two or more life cycles.

Comparing life cycles

Revise
● The children will need to understand how to make comparisons by using the phrases *similar to* and *different from*. They could begin by seeing how the growth of the hamster and nestling are similar in that both animals simply increase in size in the same way. They could compare this with the development of the frog which changes in form as the animal grows.

Assess
● Tell the children that the egg of the frog and the butterfly contains yolk and ask how this compares with the egg of a bird. (The bird's egg contains yolk too.)
● Ask the children to explain how the early development of a frog embryo differs from that of a chick. (The embryo of a tadpole has a tail and a sucker and is surrounded by a coat of jelly. The embryo of the bird develops all its body parts and is surrounded by a hard shell.)
● After these small comparisons you may like to offer wider ranging questions such as:
　● How is the life cycle of the frog similar to that of a butterfly? (They both undergo metamorphosis.)
　● How is the life cycle of a grasshopper or locust similar to that of a bird? (When the young hatch out they increase in size and retain the same basic body form.) How is it different from that of a bird? (The insect increases in size in a series of steps while the bird increases more gradually.)
　● How does the food supply of the growing young mammal differ from that of the growing nestling and fledgling? (The mammal is fed on milk until it is weaned and eats the food of the adults. The young bird is fed on the same food of the adults by the adults until it is capable of feeding itself.)
● You may like to test children who have done extensive research by asking: what is the advantage of an animal starting its life in one environment, such as the tadpole in water and the caterpillar on leaves, and living as an adult in another – the frog on land and the butterfly in the air visiting flowers? (They exploit two different food resources and the two stages do not compete for space.)

Further practice
● The children could continue identifying differences between life cycles and explaining them by comparing the life cycle of a human with an amphibian, insect and bird. You can also use the interactive activity 'Life cycles' on the CD-ROM.

Identifying invertebrates

invertebrate animal

no legs

segmented body (earthworm)

unsegmented body shell (snail)

shell (snail)

no shell (slug)

legs

less than 14 legs

6 legs (insect)

8 legs (spider)

more than 14 legs

short body (wood-louse)

long body

a pair of legs a segment (centipede)

two pairs of legs a segment (millipede)

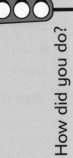

How did you do?

I can use a key to identify different invertebrates.

PHOTOCOPIABLE

Growth

- The height of a large number of people aged between 9 and 15 were measured. From this, a typical height for girls and a typical height for boys were found for each year group. The results are shown in this table:

Age	Height of girls (cm)	Height of boys (cm)
9	133	136
10	139	140
11	145	144
12	152	150
13	158	153
14	160	163
15	161	168

- On graph paper, draw one line graph showing both these sets of results. Draw the girls' line in red and the boys' line in blue.
- The diagram below shows the human body at four different ages. All the bodies have been made the same size, so you can see the proportions of the body (the amount of the total each part takes up) have changed. Describe the changes that you can see, in the proportions of each part, as a person grows.

I can describe how a human body changes as it grows.

How did you do?

Changes in the body (1)

■ These pictures show the bodies of a boy and girl who are about to start puberty. The statements at the bottom of this sheet describe the changes that will happen when one or both go through puberty. Cut out the pictures and stick them onto a large piece of paper. Cut out the statements and use them to label the pictures.

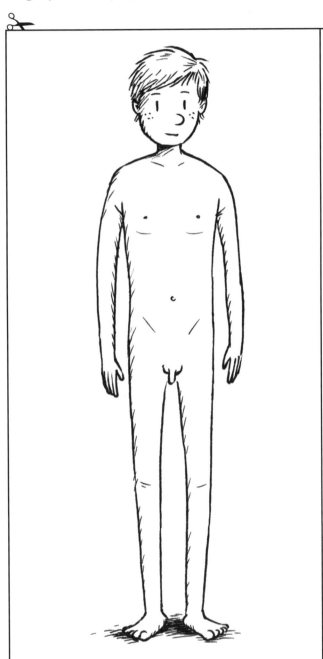
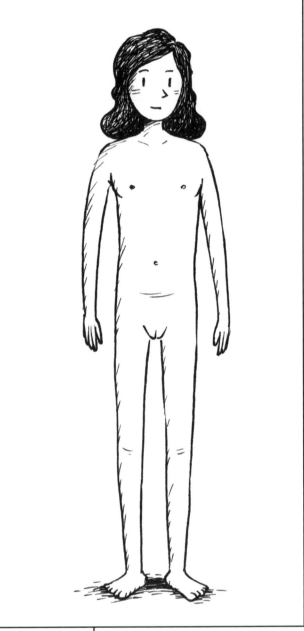

skin and hair become more oily	hips grow wider than shoulders	testicles and penis grow
hair grows between the legs	breasts and nipples grow	waist develops
skin may become spotty	hair grows in armpits	hair grows on face

The reproductive system (1)

■ Cut out the labels below and match the name of each part with its function. Cut out the diagram. Put the labels around the diagram on a sheet of paper. Check with your teacher that they are in the right places, then stick them down.

■ Draw a coloured line to show the route the egg (ovum) takes on its journey from the ovary to the uterus.

■ Under the labelled diagram, write down why you think the ovum (egg cell) is so much larger than the sperm cells that try to fertilise it.

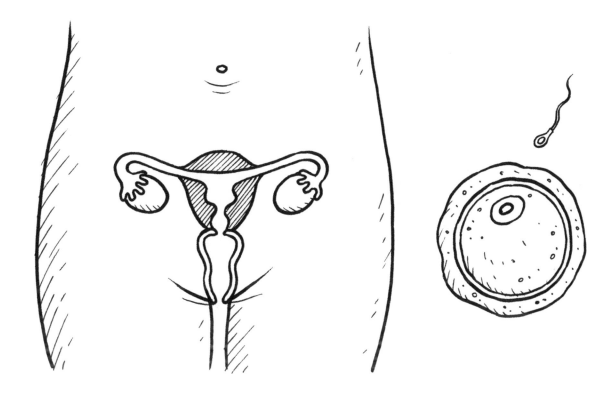

labels				
uterus	ovary	oviduct (fallopian tube)	vagina	cervix

functions	
Releases an egg (ovum) into the oviduct once every 28 days.	A special sac that provides nutrients and protection for the fertilised egg as it develops. If the female is not pregnant, the lining is shed once every 28 days during her period.
The penis releases sperm here during intercourse. The baby is born through this tube.	
The narrow entrance to the uterus through which the sperm have to travel.	The tube down which the egg is moved after it is released from the ovary. Sperm may reach and fertilise the egg here on its journey to the uterus.

The reproductive system (2)

■ Cut out the labels below and match the name of each part with its function. Cut out the diagram.

■ Put the labels around the diagram on a sheet of paper. Check with your teacher that they are in the right places, then stick them down.

■ Under the labelled diagram, write down why you think each sperm cell has a tail.

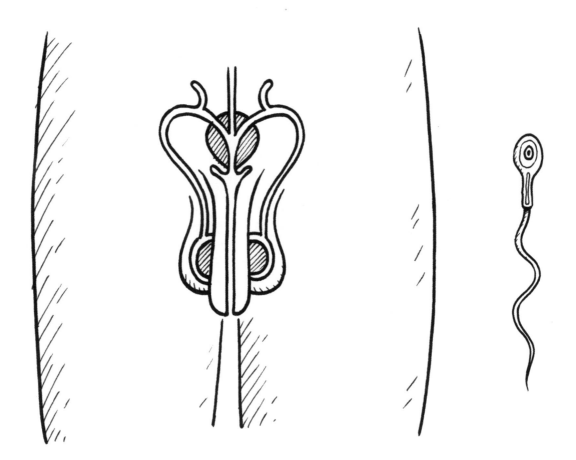

testes	penis	prostate gland	sperm tube	scrotum	labels
Becomes erect as blood rushes into it. During intercourse it enters the vagina of the female and releases sperm.		This and other glands add special chemicals to the sperm cells to make them active before they are released.			functions
Special organs that produce millions of sperm cells.		The tube down which sperm cells travel from the testes.			
The sac that contains the testes.					

PHOTOCOPIABLE   ■SCHOLASTIC www.scholastic.co.uk

Name: _____   Date: _____

The life cycle of the silver eel

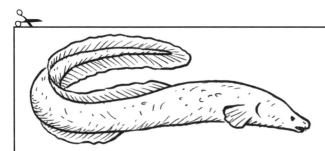

Mature eel

average male: 36cm

average female: 50cm

matures in rivers and lakes before migrating seaward, swimming west across the Atlantic Ocean

Glass eel

average length: 7cm

changes to this transparent form by the European coast and enters estuaries

Egg

average size: 1mm

eggs are hatched in the Sargasso Sea

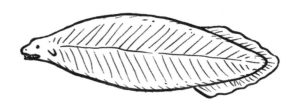

Leptocephelus

average length: 7mm

drift east across the Atlantic Ocean

Elver

average length: 6–7 cm

once established in rivers they take this form

Yellow eel

average length: 10cm

grow bigger in the rivers and change colour and shape

The desert tortoise

The desert is a cold place in winter so the desert tortoise digs a burrow almost 2m long in which to hibernate from November to February. It uses its burrows for the rest of the year to escape from the heat of the day. Males fight each other whenever they meet and will mate with females at any time. The female digs a hole in the ground to make a nest and lays up to eight eggs in it. The eggs are the size and appearance of table tennis balls (with a diameter of 4cm). The female leaves the eggs to be incubated by the warmth of the soil and after about a hundred days they hatch.

Each hatchling is about 7cm long and must find its own food and look after itself. Many become the prey of desert animals like the coyote and the raven. If a tortoise avoids predators it will grow to about 18cm in 15 years and become ready to breed.

Dame Jane Goodall

Jane Goodall was born in London in 1934. When she was a baby, her father gave her a toy chimpanzee, which she called Jubilee. She loved Jubilee and so began her love of animals. When she was four Jane went on holiday to a farm and hid in a hen house to watch hens lay eggs. When she was eight she read *The Story of Doctor Dolittle* and this inspired her to want to visit Africa.

When Jane was 12 she started her own nature club called the Alligator Society. To join the club you had to name ten types of dogs, ten birds, ten trees and five butterflies and moths. When she left school at 18 she went to work as a secretary. In 1957 Jane was invited to stay with a friend who had a farm in Kenya and while she was there she met Louis Leakey, a scientist who studied human fossils. When he heard of Jane's interest in animals he asked her to study the behaviour of a group of chimpanzees because he thought that it might help him to understand how the early forms of humans behaved.

Jane travelled to Tanzania and very patiently and bravely gained the trust of a group of chimps. Her observations of their behaviour proved to be ground-breaking. She found out that they use tools – sticks to probe termite mounds and logs to crack nuts (only humans were thought to use tools) – and that they eat monkeys (though they were thought to be herbivores). Jane looked at the chimps differently from other scientists: she gave them human names and discovered that each chimp had its own personality. Previously, scientists thought that all animals of the same species acted in the same way.

Jane returned to England and went to Cambridge University. However, she quickly returned to Tanzania where she started the Gombe Stream Research Centre. In 1977, she founded the Jane Goodall Institute for Wildlife Research, Education and Conservation, which looks at finding ways to empower individuals to protect the environment for all living things.

Properties of materials: reversible changes

Expected prior learning
- Understand the properties of a range of materials.
- Understand if an object is alive, has been alive or has never been alive.
- Know whether objects are solids, liquids or gases.
- Understand how basic electrical circuits work.

Overview of progression
By the end of this chapter children should have learned:
- to explore examples of solids, liquids and gases
- to conduct a fair test for hardness
- to create electrical circuits and test for conductivity
- to compare the insulating properties of materials
- to test for magnetic materials
- to explore the uses of a range of materials
- to find which materials are waterproof
- to investigate porosity, dissolving and evaporation
- to separate a range of mixtures, including dissolved substances.

Creative context
- There are several opportunities for children to plan investigations and link them to real, practical applications. During the lessons on solids and liquids, electrical circuits and materials and water there will be opportunities to link science and design and technology, for example, creating a 'shaky hand' machine and using microscopes to draw conclusions from close observations.
- The final lesson invites children to create scientific detective manuals, representing their understanding of mixing and separating materials.

Background knowledge
Many objects are made from more than one material and one material can be made into many objects. In deciding on what material to use it is important to consider the range of properties the material has. It may be hard or soft, heavy or light, opaque or transparent, smooth or rough, reflective or non-reflective, rigid or flexible, easily cut, shaped, moulded or stretched, magnetic or non-magnetic, able to conduct electricity or be a good insulator.

Speaking scientifically
- Children will need to know the vocabulary associated with the three states of matter as well as hardness, solubility, opacity, conductivity and magnetism.

Preparation
Many of the lessons require a range of equipment and materials (including water) prepared in advance. You will need to make sure that your classroom is set up to allow a range of experiments and there is sufficient space to leave experiments and tests until they have been finished, maybe for several days.

You will need to provide: Equipment and materials are listed for every lesson. Children will be required to work alone, in pairs and in small groups, so you will need to have lots of magnets of various shapes and strengths, a range of magnetic and non-magnetic materials, materials that will and will not conduct electricity and lots of wires, bulbs, batteries, crocodile clips, paper clips, small pieces of wood and modelling clay. The lessons on separating materials require suitable quantities of sand, gravel, soil, salt and so on, as well as ready access to water and appropriate equipment.

On the CD-ROM you will find: Photocopiable pages 'Uses of everyday materials', 'Conductors and insulators', 'Separating substances'; interactive activities 'Capillary action', 'Porosity', 'Investigating evaporation'

Chapter at a glance

Week	Lesson	Curriculum objectives	Lesson objectives	Main activity	Working scientifically
1	1	• (Y2) To identify and compare the suitability of a variety of everyday materials, including wood, metal, plastic, glass, brick, rock, paper and cardboard for particular uses. • (Y4) To compare and group materials together, according to whether they are solids, liquids or gases. • (Y4) To recognise some common conductors and insulators, and associate metals with being good conductors.	• To review the properties and uses of common everyday materials. • To revise the properties of solids and liquids. • To show how a simple electrical circuit is constructed.	Exploring objects in the classroom and the materials that they are made from. Revising the characteristics of solids and liquids and investigating solids that appear to behave like liquids. Using a simple game to revise the properties needed to make a complete circuit.	• *Using science experiences to explore ideas.* • Reporting and presenting findings from enquiries, including conclusions, causal relationships and explanations of results, in oral and written forms such as displays and other presentations.
	2	• To compare and group together everyday materials on the basis of their properties.	• To consider the properties needed for a tabletop. • To know how to test materials for hardness.	Predicting the hardness of materials and then testing them. Recording the results in written form, using diagrams.	• Planning different types of scientific enquiries to answer questions, including recognising and controlling variables where necessary. • Reporting and presenting findings from enquiries.
	3	• To compare and group together everyday materials on the basis of their properties.	• To learn about the electrical conductivity of materials.	Devising and carrying out an investigation into the electrical conductivity of materials.	• Planning different types of scientific enquiries to answer questions, including recognising and controlling variables where necessary. • Recording data and results of increasing complexity.
2	1	• To compare and group together everyday materials on the basis of their properties.	• To learn about the thermal conductivity of materials.	Testing how quickly a metal and plastic spoon conduct heat.	• Planning different types of scientific enquiries to answer questions, including recognising and controlling variables where necessary.
	2	• To compare and group together everyday materials on the basis of their properties.	• To learn about thermal conductivity and insulation.	Testing how quickly an ice cube melts and the effectiveness of different insulators.	• Using test results to make predictions to set up further comparative and fair tests.
	3	• To compare and group together everyday materials on the basis of their properties, including their hardness, solubility, transparency, conductivity (electrical and thermal), and response to magnets.	• To know the response to magnets to different materials.	Investigating materials to see whether they can be picked up by a magnet.	• Reporting and presenting findings from enquiries, including conclusions, causal relationships and explanations of results, in oral and written forms such as displays and other presentations.
3	1	• To give reasons, based on evidence from comparative and fair tests, for the particular uses of everyday materials, including metals, wood and plastic.	• To understand that the properties of everyday materials are linked with everyday use.	Surveying materials used in the school. Looking at materials that spoons can be made from and why. Looking at different types of plastic and their uses.	• Reporting and presenting findings from enquiries, including conclusions, causal relationships and explanations of results, in oral and written forms such as displays and other presentations.
	2	• To give reasons, based on evidence from comparative and fair tests, for the particular uses of everyday materials, including metals, wood and plastic.	• To understand that a number of everyday materials can be used in one object. • To know that each material used in an object is linked to its use.	Looking at the materials of a toy. Identifying the materials used in a vehicle and researching how they are made.	• *Recognising which secondary sources will be most useful to research their ideas.*
	3	• To give reasons, based on evidence from comparative and fair tests, for the particular uses of everyday materials, including metals, wood and plastic.	• To consider the waterproof properties of fabrics.	Testing fabrics to find out the properties of waterproof fabric. Planning how to make a fabric waterproof and test it.	• Planning different types of scientific enquiries to answer questions, including recognising and controlling variables where necessary.

Week	Lesson	Curriculum objectives	Lesson objectives	Main activity	Working scientifically
4	1	• To give reasons, based on evidence from comparative and fair tests, for the particular uses of everyday materials including metals, wood and plastic.	• To consider the water absorbing properties of materials.	Designing an enquiry to find out which paper towel is the most absorbent.	• Planning different types of scientific enquiries to answer questions, including recognising and controlling variables where necessary. • Taking measurements, using a range of scientific equipment.
	2	• To give reasons, based on evidence from comparative and fair tests, for the particular uses of everyday materials including metals, wood and plastic.	• To understand how water moves through some materials.	Observing how water moves through materials using capillary action.	• Reporting and presenting findings from enquiries
	3	• To use knowledge of solids, liquids and gases to decide how mixtures might be separated including through filtering, sieving and evaporating.	• To learn about porous materials, and that soil has air in it.	Investigating and comparing the amount of air in different substances.	• Identifying scientific evidence that has been used to support or refute ideas and arguments. • Reporting and presenting findings from enquiries.
5	1	• To use knowledge of solids, liquids and gases to decide how mixtures might be separated including through filtering, sieving and evaporating.	• To understand how a sieve works. • To know how a sieve can be used to separate materials.	Using a sieve to separate pebbles from a mixture. Devising, making and using a sieve to separate aquarium gravel from sand.	• Reporting and presenting findings from enquiries.
	2	• To use knowledge of solids, liquids and gases to decide how mixtures might be separated including through filtering, sieving and evaporating. • To demonstrate reversible changes.	• To know how particles of different sizes can form different layers of sediment, and that this process can be used to separate materials.	Investigating the use of sedimentation in soil analysis, and compare this to using sieves to try and separate the components of a soil.	• Reporting and presenting findings from enquiries, including conclusions, causal relationships and explanations of results, in oral and written forms such as displays and other presentations.
	3	• To know that some materials will dissolve in liquid to form a solution, and describe how to recover a substance from a solution.	• To understand that when some mixtures mix with water some of their components may dissolve. • To identify substances which are soluble and insoluble in water.	Exploring sedimentation as a way of separating all the components in soil. Mixing substances with water and identifying those that dissolve and those that do not.	• Planning different types of scientific enquiries to answer questions, including recognising and controlling variables where necessary. • Recording data and results of increasing complexity.
6	1	• To know that some materials will dissolve in liquid to form a solution, and describe how to recover a substance from a solution. • To use knowledge of solids, liquids and gases to decide how mixtures might be separated through evaporating.	• To know that evaporation can be used as a means of recovering a dissolved solid.	Explaining how evaporation could be used to recover dissolved substances. Investigating the use of evaporation in the formation of crystals of Epsom salts.	• Reporting and presenting findings from enquiries, including conclusions, causal relationships and explanations of results, in oral and written forms such as displays and other presentations.
	2	• To use knowledge of solids, liquids and gases to decide how mixtures might be separated, through filtering, and evaporating. • To demonstrate reversible changes.	• To learn how mixing, dissolving, filtering and evaporation can be used in separating materials.	Devising and carrying out an investigation to see if filtering and evaporation can be used to separate sand and salt.	• Identifying scientific evidence that has been used to support or refute ideas or arguments. • Reporting and presenting findings from enquiries.
	3	• To use knowledge of solids, liquids and gases to decide how mixtures might be separated, including through filtering, sieving and evaporating. • To demonstrate reversible changes.	• To demonstrate knowledge of reversible changes.	Reviewing learning from the chapter to produce a detective manual based on new knowledge.	• They should use relevant scientific language and illustrations to discuss, communicate and justify their scientific ideas.
Assess and review					

■SCHOLASTIC

Objectives
- To review the properties and uses of common everyday materials.
- To revise the properties of solids, liquids and gases.
- To show how a simple electrical circuit is constructed.

Resources
An old object likely to be unfamiliar to the children; hand lenses; sugar; water; a number of containers; modelling dough; sticky tape; electrical wire; wire; batteries; bulbs; bulb holders; crocodile clips; buzzers; photocopiable page 69 'The shaky-hand machine'

Speaking scientifically
materials, solid, liquid, circuit

Lesson 1: What do we know about materials?

Introduction

Show the children the old object and ask them to think what it might have been used for. Talk about what it looks like and feels like. Ask them to identify any of the materials it is made from. Encourage the children to use this information to try to identify the object. Tell the children that they are now going to find out about other, more familiar, objects in the classroom.

Group work

1. Give the children one minute to write down all the materials they can touch without moving from their seat and then another minute to write down materials they can see in the classroom. Point out that almost all the materials will have been solids. For example, plastic for chairs and tabletops, metal for table legs, door handles, door hinges, wood for doors, window frames, fabrics for carpets and their clothes.

2. Ask questions about why particular materials have been used, for example: *Why is plastic used for chairs? Why not metal, paper or fabric? Why don't people wear iron gloves?* They need to be aware that solids have properties that make them good for certain things. Ask if anyone has written down that they could touch a gas – the air they breathe.

3. Remind the children that there are three states of matter and ask them to tell you what these are (solids, liquids and gases).

Whole-class work

4. Ask: *What can you tell me about solids and liquids?* Look for answers that solids can't be poured, have a fixed shape and do not change shape as you pick them up, while liquids can be poured and change shape easily, taking the shape of the container that they are poured into.

5. Ask the children to name examples of solids and liquids and to describe their characteristic. (*Are they rigid? Can they flow? How easy is it to change their shape?*)

6. Show the children the sugar and ask: *Is this a solid or a liquid?* Pour the sugar into different containers and watch how it takes the shape of each container. Explain to the children that sometimes solids can be poured when they are in lots of small pieces.

Group work

7. Give out the hand lenses and let the children examine the individual granules of sugar. Encourage them to feel them so that they realise that they are made of small solid particles.

8. Let them pour water into a container and sugar into another container and ask them to note the differences between how the solid and liquid behaves. (They should see that the solid pours into a cone shape.)

Whole-class work

9. Remind the children how electricity flows from the positive end of the battery back to the negative end, but it can only flow through wires that make up a circuit.

10. Ask them what happens if there is a break in the circuit. They should know that the current will not flow because the electricity won't be able to pass the break.

Checkpoint
● Can children identify any solid objects in this room?
● Can children describe the simple physical properties of objects around them?
● Do they know that there are three states of matter?
● Do they know the properties that solids and liquids have?
● Do the children know how electricity flows?
● Are they able to construct a simple series electrical circuit?
● Do the children know some common conductors and insulators?
● Do they know that metal is a good conductor?

Group or independent work

11. Organise the children into groups of four and give them wires, a battery, a bulb, bulb holder and crocodile clips and sticky tape.

12. Tell them that you want them to make a circuit that lights up the bulb. Explain that they don't have to use all the materials to create the circuit.

13. Once they have created their circuit, ask them to show it to you. Then encourage them to draw their own circuit as a labelled diagram and write a description of what they did and why it worked.

14. When they have finished their work on their basic circuits, give each group photocopiable page 69 'The shaky-hand machine' and the equipment needed to make the machine.

15. When children have made the machine, ensure that they are familiar with the game: the aim is to pass the small loop of wire along the bendy wire without touching it.

16. Explain that if the wire touches, the buzzer sounds and they have to start again.

17. Ask: *Why does the buzzer sound?* They should know that it is because if the two wires touch they have formed an unbroken circuit.

18. When they have tried each other's machines, ask them to draw and describe what they did and how their shaky-hand machine works.

Introducing the new area of study

Explain that children are going to extend their knowledge of solids by exploring and comparing a range of materials. Ask: *Why is it useful to know about the properties of materials?* Refer back to the objects in the classroom and discuss the characteristics that you might want to know about in materials and list them on the board (hardness, strength, changing shape, opacity, weight, conductivity, magnetism, absorbency).

Differentiation
● Support children who find making the circuits and the shaky-hand machine difficult. Give them practical help in joining wires and connecting buzzers and bulbs and so on.
● Challenge children to design a test to show the presence of air.

Science in the wider world

All materials are made from natural resources – even man-made ones! Many materials are made from scarce resources such as oil, wood and iron ore. These resources are not finite and may run out.

Review

Ask some children to demonstrate pouring sugar and water and explain the similarities and differences. Other children can show their shaky-hand machines and explain what they did.

Lesson 2: Testing for hardness

Objectives
• To consider the properties needed for a tabletop.
• To know how to test materials for hardness.

Resources
Small samples (two of each and enough for the class to be divided into groups of four) of the following materials: chalk; wood (lollipop stick) wax candle; pieces of chocolate; piece of chalk; flat pieces of metal; large amount of modelling dough; paper; pencils

Speaking scientifically
harness, fair test, scratch, materials, properties

Introduction
Investigate what some common objects are made from. Chairs will probably be plastic on metal legs, windows will be glass in either a wood or metal frame, clothes will be wool, cotton or man-made fabrics. Ask: *Why have certain materials been used? What properties do your clothes have?* (They will need to be soft and flexible and give a certain amount of protection from wind, rain and cold, for example.) Ask: *Why aren't the windows made from paper with a cotton frame?* (Paper and cotton don't have the properties that a window needs. They need to be rigid and transparent.)

Whole-class work
1. Ask the children to tell you the properties of the material used to make the tops of their tables or desks. (They need to be smooth, rigid and hard.) Ask them why they have to have all of these properties.

2. Ask them what other materials could be used for their tabletops. (They should mention plastic, wood or metal as being hard materials.) Ask: *How do you know that the material is hard?*

Group work
3. Give out the materials to the children and tell them that they are going to test them for hardness and try to find out which one is the hardest and which is the softest. Ask them to anticipate what the results of the test might be.

4. Explain that they have to roll out the modelling dough to form a flat surface large enough to press all the items into it, leaving a gap between them.

5. Next, they should use each material, in turn, to scratch down across all the others. There should be space on each of the materials to show all the scratch marks.

6. When they have done this ask: *Which material could scratch itself and the modelling dough but nothing else?* (chocolate) *Which material could scratch everything?* (metal) *Which material could scratch almost everything?* (plastic)

Independent work
7. Ask the children to write down what they have done using labelled diagrams and sentences to explain their results, checking whether their results matched their predictions and concluding which were the hardest and softest materials.

Differentiation
• Support children who need help in setting out their hardness test. They may also need help in writing their results.
• Challenge children to devise a fair test to find out the hardness of floor coverings.

Science in the wider world
Diamonds used to be the hardest material on Earth until scientists manufactured harder nanomaterials. Scientists have also been testing some very rare natural materials that are thought to be the hardest substance ever measured – wurtzite boron nitrade (formed during volcanic eruptions) and lonsdaleite (formed when meteorites containing graphite hit the Earth).

Review
Ask some children to present their reports to the rest of the class. Talk about how accurate their initial predictions were and the importance of fair testing and experiments to find out answers to questions.

Objectives
● To learn about the electrical conductivity of materials.

Resources
Photocopiable page 70 'Making it flow'; battery; bulb; bulb holder; wires (plastic coated with ends bared); crocodile clips (enough for one set for each group of four); a variety of materials for testing such as string; elastic bands; plastic pen tops; stainless steel cutlery; wire; pencil lead

Speaking scientifically
current, flow, conduct, conductivity, circuit

Lesson 3: Testing for electrical conductivity

Introduction
Draw some circuits on the board – some that will work and some that have pieces missing and gaps in the circuit so that they will not work. For each one, ask the children why the electrical current will or will not flow. Establish that the current will not flow if there is any kind of gap in the circuit.

Whole-class work
1. Tell each group to make a circuit that will work and check that they can do this. Ask them why it works.

2. Now tell each group to bend the wire so that the ends to be connected are now plastic. Ask them what will happen if they connect the circuit using the plastic ends of the wires. (They should know that the circuit won't work because the current can't flow because the plastic won't conduct electricity.) Ask them to connect the circuit just to prove that the current won't flow.

Group work
3. Give each child photocopiable page 70 'Making it flow' and explain how to complete it. The group can test each object for conductivity but each child has to write down their own results.

4. Remind them that if the object conducts electricity, the circuit will be complete and the bulb will light up. If the object doesn't conduct electricity there will be a gap in the circuit and the current will not flow.

5. When they have finished, check that everyone has the same results.

Differentiation
● Support children who need help in understanding how electricity flows and might find making their circuits and completing their chart on the photocopiable sheet difficult. They will need practical help.
● Challenge children to think about electricity in their homes. For example, ask: *Why are light switches often made of plastic? Why are plugs plastic and not metal? Why are wires and cables either rubber or plastic?*

Science in the wider world
Knowing which materials conduct electricity and which don't is very important when using electricity. Most metals are good conductors of electricity, while most plastics aren't. Therefore, metal wires are covered with plastic (insulators) in order to stop people being electrocuted. Similarly plugs on appliances that we touch when we plug them into sockets are made of plastic. It is only the parts that have to connect to the electrical circuits that are made of metal.

Review
Ask some volunteers to explain to the rest of the class how to construct a circuit and why it works. Are there some objects that conducted electricity which they thought wouldn't?

Objectives

● To learn about the thermal conductivity of materials.

Resources

A mug of hot water (not boiling); plastic spoon; metal spoon; a stopwatch; hot-water bottles; a range of materials: wood, plastic, paper, cardboard, metal; photocopiable page 71 'Travelling heat'; access to a freezer (preferably a small one that can be kept in the classroom); access to a hot radiator

Speaking scientifically

materials, temperature, heat, conductors, thermal conductors

Lesson 1: Testing for thermal conductivity (1)

Introduction

Explain that heat travels through materials and is always trying to escape. It travels from hot spots to colder areas and it travels through some materials faster than others.

The materials that heat passes through quickly are called good thermal conductors.

Whole-class work

1. Ask the children whether they think that metal or plastic is a better thermal conductor.

2. Fill a mug with very hot water (not boiling – but take care) and immediately put a metal spoon and a plastic spoon in the water. One volunteer should hold the metal spoon and one hold the plastic spoon. Start the stopwatch and tell the volunteers to let go as soon as they feel heat in their spoons.

3. Explain that the heat from the water will have passed through the spoons – the metal spoon should heat up much faster than the plastic one because it is a better thermal conductor.

Group work

4. Using hot-water bottles filled with hot (not boiling) water (ensure that the top is screwed on tightly), each group should lay each of the materials, in turn, on top of the hot-water bottle and time how long it takes for them to feel the heat.

5. When the heat has transferred through the material the children should stop the stopwatch and write down the time alongside the material. If necessary, keep reheating the hot-water bottles.

6. Ask the children to explain which of the materials was the best thermal conductor (fastest heat transfer) and which one was the worst.

7. Give each child photocopiable page 71 'Travelling heat' and ask them to complete it in their groups, but to write down their own answers.

Differentiation

● Support children who find the practical parts of this lesson confusing – timing the heat transfer and completing their sheets.
● Challenge children to find out as much as possible about insulation in houses. *Why do houses need insulation – what is it for and what is it made from?*

Science in the wider world

Energy to heat houses is expensive and houses that are made from good thermal conductors will lose their heat rapidly because it will escape. Thermal insulation that traps heat is essential.

Review

When the children have finished the sheet, go through them with the whole class and check that they all have similar results.

Objectives
● To learn about thermal conductivity and insulation.

Resources
Small containers (three for each group of four children); ice cubes (enough for all the containers); materials such as woollen jumper; foil; newspaper; polystyrene; hot water (not boiling); tea cosy or woolly hat; watches; thermometers; internet access

Speaking scientifically
thermal conductor, thermal insulator, temperature, insulation

Lesson 2: Testing for thermal conductivity (2)

Introduction
Remind the children that when they placed materials onto a hot-water bottle, the different materials absorbed the heat and some were better thermal conductors than others. Ask: *Which materials were the quickest to absorb the heat?* Talk about how the hot-water bottle gradually got colder because the heat was lost. Ask them where they think the heat from the hot-water bottle went and write their ideas on the board.

Whole-class work
1. Explain that we often try to stop heat from moving about. Sometimes we use materials to keep heat in – sometimes to keep heat out. Say that the materials we use are good thermal insulators.

2. Explain that you want them to test different materials to find the best one to keep heat out (the best thermal insulator).

Group work
3. Allow the children to choose three containers and a selection of materials. Quickly place an ice cube into each of their three containers and tell them to wrap different materials round each of the containers in order to try to keep the heat out and to stop the ice cube from melting.

4. Once the containers are wrapped with three different materials, the children should time how long it takes for the ice cube in each container to melt. They should then draw conclusions about which is the best thermal insulator. (The one that melts the fastest is wrapped with a poor thermal insulator and the one that melts the slowest is wrapped in a good thermal insulator.)

5. Now ask the children to use their results to predict which materials would be the best at minimising heat loss. They should devise a test using containers of hot water (not boiling), materials and a thermometer to prove that insulation works.

6. Tell the children to write up their experiments using diagrams to help them explain what happened.

Differentiation
● Support children who find thermal conductivity and insulation difficult to understand by explaining it in more detail. They might also need help with their diagrams and explanations.
● Challenge children to find out how thick the insulation should be in their lofts at home.

Science in the wider world
Energy costs are very expensive and so modern homes use many different materials, both natural and manufactured, as thermal insulation. The most popular materials are: fibreglass, mineral wool, cellulose (made from recycled paper and cardboard), polyurethane foam and straw bales.

Review
Ask some of the groups to present their findings to the rest of the class.

■■SCHOLASTIC

Objectives
● To know the response to magnets of different materials.

Resources
Bar magnets (one for every child with spares for each table); paper clips (a pile for each group); a collection of materials including coins; rubbers; glass; pins; pencils; nails, and so on; photocopiable page 72 'Magnetic forces'; internet access

Speaking scientifically
magnet, poles, repel, attract, prediction, result

Lesson 3: Testing for magnetic materials

Introduction
Show the children the bar magnets and ask them what a magnet is. Write any relevant answers on the whiteboard. They need to understand that a bar magnet exerts a force – the magnetic force. Explain that it has a pushing effect (it repels other magnetic materials) and a pulling effect (it attracts other magnetic materials). These attracting and repelling forces are strongest at the two ends of the bar magnets – the north and the south poles.

Whole-class work
1. Make sure that each child has a bar magnet and that there are spares on each table. Ask them to put two north poles together and see what happens – then two south poles, and then a north and a south pole. (Like poles repel and unlike poles attract.)

2. Ask them what kind of materials they think will be attracted to a magnet. (They should know that materials made from some metals such as iron and steel can be picked up by a magnet.)

3. Show the children a paper clip. Ask them to predict whether it will be attracted or repelled by the magnet.

Group work
4. Put a handful of paper clips on each table and ask them to see whether their prediction was true or not.

5. Show the children some of the materials that they will test in order to find out whether they will be attracted to the magnets. Tell them to predict whether the materials will be attracted.

6. Give each child a photocopiable page 72 'Magnetic forces' to complete.

Differentiation
● Most children should be able to understand this lesson without support, but the photocopiable sheet might need to be simplified or explained more slowly or even read to some children.
● Challenge children to use secondary sources to find out more about how magnets are used in machines and ask them to find out why magnets are different shapes.

Science in the wider world
Our world would be very different without magnets. They are used for all sorts of things from compasses and everyday appliances to high-speed maglev trains. Maglev trains use magnets instead of wheels that repel against magnets in the tracks lifting and thrusting the train along.

Review
Talk about the materials that were attracted to the magnets and ask how accurate their predictions were. Ask: *Would you be able to predict more accurately which materials would be attracted to a magnet now? Why?*

Objectives
● To understand that the properties of everyday materials are linked with everyday use.

Resources
Paper and pencils; wooden, plastic and metal spoons – as many different kinds of plastic materials as possible; photocopiable page 73 'Useful plastic'

Speaking scientifically
materials, properties, transparent

Lesson 1: Uses of materials in school

Introduction
Remind the children that materials are used to make things because they have the right properties. Give them a few ridiculous examples that show that certain properties are needed for certain objects. For example ask: *Why aren't teapots made of paper? Why aren't hammers made from glass? Why aren't umbrellas made of lead? Why aren't your gloves made from metal or rubber?*

Whole-class work
1. Check that the children know some of the properties of common materials – wood is hard and can be shaped, metal is rigid, fabrics are soft and can be sewn together and so on.

2. Ask them to write down the headings: *Wood, Metal, Stone, Plastic* and *Fabric* on a piece of paper.

3. Tell them that they are going to walk around the school and list the objects that they see under the different headings, according to the main material that they are made from.

4. Back in the classroom, make a whole-class list on the board. Ask: *Why is wood used in doors? Why are some floors covered in plastic tiles and others covered in carpets? Why are the windows made from glass and metal or glass and plastic? Why are your clothes made from cotton or wool?*

5. Show the children the different spoons. Ask: *Why are they made from different materials?* Talk about what spoons are used for and how each of the materials meets the requirements of a spoon.

Group work
6. Explain that although different materials can be used for the same object, often the choice of material relates to cost. Point out that they will probably have found more objects that are made of plastic than other materials although other materials would have the right properties.

7. Give each child photocopiable page 73 'Useful plastic' and ask each of them to complete it but to talk about what their answers are going to be with other children before writing them down.

8. Use objects you have brought into the classroom or items that they have found in school.

> ### Differentiation
> ● Support children in accurately identifying the materials that objects are made from and in reading the photocopiable sheet.
> ● Challenge children to identify common objects that can be made from a range of materials such as, carpets (synthetic and natural fibres), crockery, cutlery and so on.

Science in the wider world
Natural materials, such as wood, are biodegradeable and rot when they are thrown away. The problem with most man-made materials, like plastics, is that they don't rot away and so cause pollution. However, biodegradeable plastics are now being made but they are more expensive to make.

Review
Ask some children to explain to the class what certain parts of their homes are made of. For example, they could tell the class about their bedroom and all the materials that are used in it, such as wood for the bed and furniture, glass in the windows, different fabrics for the carpets and bedcovers, paper on the wall and so on.

Objectives
● To understand that a number of everyday materials can be used in one object.
● To know that each material used in an object is linked to its use.

Resources
Large toy that is made from different materials; pictures from magazines of different vehicles; secondary sources on how different materials are made; large sheets of paper (one for each pair); several smaller sheets for each pair; scissors; adhesive; pencils and coloured pencils

Speaking scientifically
materials, properties, manufactured

Lesson 2: Uses of materials in the wider world

Introduction
Show the class the toy and ask them what it is made from. Write down the materials on the board. Ask questions about why each material has been used, for example: *Why are the tyres rubber? Why is the frame metal? What are the bolts made from?* Remind the children that the properties of a material will determine what it is used for.

Whole-class work
1. On the board draw a quick diagram of the toy and ask for volunteers to point to plastic parts, wooden parts, rubber parts and so on.

2. Each time they point to a specific part, draw a line from that part to a space away from the drawing and write the name of the material. You should end up with a series of lines going from the actual toy to each of the materials.

3. Without using any secondary sources at this stage, ask the children if they know how each part would have been made. Each time they give you some relevant information write it down on the board: for example, alongside the metal/steel label you might have written iron ore – dug out of the ground – heated in a furnace and so on.

Paired work
4. Ask each pair to choose a common 'object' that everyone knows and can recognise, for example a bicycle, car, motorbike, bus and so on.

5. Using the magazine pictures, let the children choose one of the examples, cut out a good picture of it and stick it in the centre of a large piece of paper, leaving plenty of room around it.

6. They then have to identify what different parts are made from and join lines to a space around the outside.

7. For each material, they must use a small piece of paper to say why they think this particular material has been used and then find out from the secondary sources how it has been made. Write the process down using diagrams if appropriate and stick it to the large sheet.

Differentiation
● Support children who have problems finding appropriate secondary sources and using them to find information about the materials they have found. Help them to choose appropriate books and online information.
● Challenge children to find out how other materials are manufactured. For example, petrol, glass and wool, as well as materials used in cooking such as sugar and flour.

Science in the wider world
Consumerism is about using more and more of the world's natural resources. The children should start thinking about how we can use less and recycle more.

Review
When they have finished, all the sheets can be mounted as part of a whole class display. Encourage each pair to talk about their work to the rest of the class.

• To consider the waterproof properties of fabrics.

Resources
A collection of old waterproof coats and a range of different fabrics; coloured paper; pipettes; 10cm² squares of cotton fabric; small containers for water; water; wax candles; polythene

Speaking scientifically
properties, materials, waterproof membrane

Lesson 3: Which materials are waterproof?

Introduction

Remind the children that all of the materials that are used in the classroom and in their houses are always chosen for a specific property. Explain that the same applies to fabrics used in clothing. Talk about the winter and the need to keep warm and dry and the fact that when it rains we need something that is waterproof. Ask: *What does waterproof mean?* (Water is unable to go through it.)

Whole-class work

1. At the front of the class place a piece of ordinary cotton over a piece of coloured paper and drop water from the pipette on to it. The water will quickly soak through and soak the coloured paper.

2. Do the same thing with a piece of the waterproof fabric from one of the old raincoats. The water will either not soak through at all – or it will soak through very slowly.

3. Tell the children that waterproof materials have usually been treated with something (like wax) or will have a built-in membrane that stops water from soaking through.

Group work

4. Tell the children that you want them to find out which of the fabrics in your collection is the most waterproof.

5. Ask them to choose and number three fabrics, and repeat the process that you demonstrated to them. When they have finished, they should write down what they have done in a way that shows the waterproof fabric for other children to see.

6. Give each group two cotton squares, a candle and a sheet of polythene and ask them to make the cotton waterproof. (They should realise that if they rub the candle across the cotton several times the wax will soak into the material. The polythene can be placed on top or underneath the cotton to create a waterproof membrane.)

7. Tell them to write down what they did using labelled diagrams and whether it worked.

Differentiation
• Support children who need help to test the different materials and write up their experiment. Other children in the group could help but make sure you talk to each group.
• Challenge children to find out what problems might be caused by using a membrane like polythene (high levels of perspiration).

Science in the wider world

Manufacturers have realised that not only should rainwear be waterproof, but it should also be breathable to stop people getting wet from the inside rather than from the outside! Manufacturers also tape over the seams of garments to ensure that water cannot leak through them.

Review

Some groups could explain to the rest of the class or to another class what they did and what happened.

Objectives
● To consider the water absorbing properties of materials.

Resources
Different materials (such as cotton, wool, canvas); bowls; water, different papers (such as tissues; wrapping paper; writing paper); paper towels (ranging from economy to expensive varieties and including one that is made from recycled paper); permanent marker pens; a strip of blotting paper; stopwatches; measuring jugs

Speaking scientifically
liquid, absorb, measure, millilitres, material, absorbent

Lesson 1: Comparing how materials absorb water

Introduction

Remind the children about what they did when they were looking for the waterproofing properties of different materials. Ask: *What properties would you look for in a raincoat?* Then ask when you might want to use a material that is the opposite of waterproof (absorbent).

Whole-class work

1. Show the class the range of different materials. Ask: *Which materials absorb water?* They should know from the previous lesson that some of the materials that make anoraks and cagoules are waterproof. Ask: *Is it possible to tell which material will absorb the most water?*

2. Place some bowls (one containing water) where the children can see them. Dip a range of materials and papers into the water and use the other bowls to drain the water into.

3. Dip a range of paper towels into the water and observe how some papers disintegrate. Ask: *Why is that?* (They are only able to absorb so much water. If they take in too much they disintegrate and fall apart.)

Group work

4. Ask the children to plan a test to find out which paper is the best at absorbing water without disintegrating. Ask: *What kind of paper is made so that it will absorb water?* (blotting paper, kitchen paper, paper towels)

5. Tell the children that they will be testing different kitchen papers and remind them that it needs to be a fair test. Also ensure that they number the papers in one of the corners with a permanent marker so that they know which paper is which.

6. Give the children instructions similar to these for their test:

7. Use two sheets from each roll.

8. Lay the paper flat on the surface of the water and push down for 30 seconds.

9. Take out and immediately squeeze the paper for 10 seconds into the measuring jug.

10. Measure the water in the jug in millilitres and write it down alongside the number of the paper.

11. Empty the jug and repeat this with all the numbered papers.

12. When they have finished the test they need to write up how they did it, including diagrams and instructions and their results in a table.

> **Differentiation**
> ● Support any children who might find doing the fair test difficult and who might not be able to write up their test without adult help.
> ● Challenge children to devise a test to show if bricks or unfired clay absorb water.

Science in the wider world

Certain materials are made for a specific purpose and some materials like paper towels are widely used. The paper they are made of is different to the paper that you write on. Paper towels are loosely woven and writing paper tightly made so that it is smooth and shiny.

Review

Ask the children to talk about how well each type of paper absorbed water. Ask: *Did the most expensive paper absorb the most water? Did the cheapest absorb the least water? How well did the recycled paper do? Did each group have the same results? If not, why not?*

Objectives
• To understand how water moves through some materials.

Resources
Water coloured with food colouring; paper towels; teaspoon; clear jars; celery sticks; magnifying lenses; internet access; interactive activity 'Capillary action' on the CD-ROM

Speaking scientifically
capillary action, chromatography, cohesion, surface tension

Lesson 2: Moving water

Introduction

Spill a small amount of water on a plastic table and lay a paper towel on it. The children will know from the previous lesson that the paper towel is absorbing the water. Ask: *Where does the water go when it leaves the top of the table?* It goes into the paper towel, but how?

Whole-class work

1. Tell the children that the water moves into the paper towel because of something called 'capillary action'.

2. Put a teaspoon of water on the tabletop and ask why it doesn't spread all over the table. Explain that it is held together by cohesion – a force that pulls the droplets together. The water droplets on the edge cling more tightly to the droplets around them. This is known as surface tension.

3. When these forces of cohesion and surface tension are more powerful than gravity, the water can climb into small tubes and small spaces in different materials. This is called capillary action.

4. Put a teaspoon of coloured water onto the plastic tabletop and dip the corner of a vertical paper towel into it. The coloured water will climb into the paper towel using capillary action.

5. Before you start the paired work make sure that the children realise that water will spread and be absorbed by a paper towel laid flat on the water and it will also rise up into the material using capillary action.

Paired work

6. Explain that capillary action can be seen clearly using celery. Give each pair some coloured water in a clear jar and two sticks of celery. Tell the children to look at the cut ends of the celery through their lenses. They should see the tiny holes that help the plant absorb water.

7. Ask them what they think will happen if they place the celery sticks in the coloured water. Over a few hours, the capillary action should draw the coloured water into the stalk.

8. Tell the children to draw what they did and to explain what happened, using the term 'capillary action'.

> **Differentiation**
> • Support children who find the concepts difficult and explain the terms that were used again. When writing about the celery experiment, encourage them to give a full explanation of capillary action and use the terms *surface tension* and *cohesion*. You could also use the interactive activity 'Capillary action' on the CD-ROM.
> • Challenge children to look up chromatography and explain what it is.

Science in the wider world

Sponges work because of capillary action. They take in water through small tubes inside the sponges. When areas of soil are wet and some areas close by are dry, capillary action allows water to flow from the wet soil to the dry. Water in the ground can rise up through the foundations of buildings using capillary action. All houses and buildings have damp courses to prevent the water from rising.

Review

Remind children that sponges and paper towels absorb water because they are materials that have tiny spaces in them for the water to rise and soak in. Their writing paper is cleverly designed to have some small holes but not many – just enough for some ink to soak in before it dries.

Objectives
● To learn about porous materials and that soil has air in it.

Resources
A sponge; beakers; a see-through tank or tray; water; a range of containers for holding water; a collection of marbles; stones; sand; gravel; measuring spoons; measuring cylinders; photocopiable page 74 'Investigating porosity'; interactive activity 'Porosity' on the CD-ROM

Speaking scientifically
gas, insoluble, liquid, particle, permeate, porous, porosity, solid

Lesson 3: Porous materials

Introduction
Pass a sponge around the class. Ask: *Why is it so light? Why does it change shape when squeezed?* Say that it is porous, meaning that it contains air. The sponge has lots of gaps in it which is filled with air, the gas all around us. Challenge the children to suggest ideas for how you might capture all of the air that is inside the sponge. Collate ideas, and then demonstrate by holding a beaker with its open end downwards in a tank of water, ensuring that it has no trapped air in it. Hold the sponge underneath the beaker with your other hand and squeeze it. (The air in the sponge will be forced out, and as it rises it will be caught in the beaker.) Keeping the beaker underwater, look at how much air is inside it, and compare this to the volume of the sponge.

Whole-class work
1. Explain the terms 'porous' and 'porosity', the latter being 'how much' a material is porous. Explain that the gaps in materials such as soil are typically full of air, but can be replaced by water.

2. Take a container and fill it with marbles. Ask the children if it is full or not, and what is in it, eliciting that there are marbles and air. Demonstrate how to measure the air between the marbles. Take a set amount of water in a measuring cylinder and pour it into the container full of marbles. When the water appears at the surface all the air has been displaced (there may be bubbles that rise through the marbles and water).

3. Demonstrate how to calculate the volume of water in the marbles by subtracting the remaining water in the cylinder from the original amount.

Group work
4. In groups of three to five, give each group photocopiable page 74 'Investigating porosity'. Allow them five minutes or so to plan their experiment and list the equipment they require.

5. Before they start working, discuss the amounts of each material type that will be needed, as well as how to ensure a fair test. Remind the children that once the materials have had water added they cannot be used for a second test, and should be returned to separate containers to dry out for reuse on another occasion.

6. Explain that the repeated tests required by the chart are to ensure accuracy and consistency. If their results differ significantly they may need further tests.

> **Differentiation**
> ● Support children by ensuring that they work methodically so that all children can keep track of the experiments as well as having opportunities to measure water and calculate the amount of displaced air.
> ● Challenge children to calculate how much water a cubic metre of soil/gravel/sand would hold. Use the interactive activity 'Porosity' on the CD-ROM to check understanding of the basic concept.

Science in the wider world
Understanding porosity is very important to geologists and water engineers. They use it to predict and measure where levels of groundwater are, helping them to predict if we will have enough water for our daily needs.

Review
Were children's results as expected? How much did porosity differ between materials?

Remind the children of previous discussions about water filtration. Can they see what role each of the substances tested might have?

Objectives
● To understand how a sieve works.
● To know how a sieve can be used to separate materials.

Resources
A large bowl; pebbles; aquarium gravel; sand; a large-holed sieve (suitable for separating pebbles); a set of sieves (optional); large trays for holding and collecting sieved materials; a collection of everyday sieves and meshes; string; tweezers and other paraphernalia that may or may not be useful for constructing sieves

Speaking scientifically
filter, particle, sieve

Lesson 1: Separating sand and gravel

Introduction
Discuss the different ways that the children are sorted everyday at school, by age in each year group, by gender for using the toilets, and so on. Say they are going to walk to the shops. Ask where they might encounter sorting on their journey? (pavements and traffic lanes; different shops for different items; goods on shelves) Point out that when buying clothes we use labels to help us choose the correct size – without these we would have to use our judgement or trial and error.

Whole-class work
1. In a large bowl, create a mixture in front of the children, mixing pebbles, aquarium gravel and sand. Discuss each material, considering what it is made from, where you might find it, particle size and so on.

2. Ask how the pebbles could be removed from the mixture. Start removing them by hand, and consider the difficulties and problems. Next, use a large sieve to separate the pebbles from the mixture, and consider if this is more effective, but also if it has any drawbacks (damaging the materials).

Group work
3. Tell the children that you want them to work out how to separate sand from gravel. Ideally you will have a wide range of materials to assist them – especially different meshes and collecting trays, but also equipment that is less useful (such as tweezers) so that groups can eliminate items too. Allow them to use water if they think of it.

4. If it is impractical to carry out this experiment in your classroom, ask children to plan an experiment, then discuss each group's plans to consider viability, carrying out one at a time with the children observing.

Differentiation
● Support some children by providing them with a commercial sieve set to ensure that they perceive the correct use of sieves.
● Challenge children by providing a range of mixtures to be sieved, such as flour and sugar, different types of nuts or dried pulses. Ask them to prepare brief reports stating the range of sieves that would be needed to separate each mixture.

Science in the wider world
Sieves are used for sorting, separating and sizing all kinds of raw materials from diamonds to cacao beans. Filters are also a type of sieve and they are used to capture minute particles, such as dust and pollen, to remove them from the air, and filtration beds are used to clean water – we depend on them all the time!

Review
Ask children to explain the reasons and causes for their decisions and events, using appropriate vocabulary. What issues did they consider in planning their work? What problems did they encounter in carrying out their work? What recommendations would they make for others who might do the same task?

■ SCHOLASTIC

Objectives
● To know how particles of different sizes can form different layers of sediment, and that this process can be used to separate materials.

Resources
A large bowl; a mixture of pebbles; aquarium gravel and sand; a set of sorting sieves; three transparent containers; soil containing stones, gravel, sand and/or clay; water; a glass mixing jar; a stirrer; a video or digital camera (optional), photocopiable page 75 'Separating solids'

Speaking scientifically
filter, particle, sediment, sieve, soil

Lesson 2: Separating a range of particles in a mixture

Introduction
Remind the children of the work they did separating different-sized particles in the previous lesson. Repeat the experiment using a set of sorting sieves, tipping the separated contents into three containers (ideally transparent) where they can be easily seen.

Stack the containers in the order that the materials were separated: stones on top, then gravel, then sand. Discuss why they appeared in this order, and what would have happened if the sieve order had been reversed (nothing).

Emphasise that the sorting activity was based on particle size.

Whole-class work
1. Using a large glass mixing jar, add around one-quarter soil to three-quarters water, and then shake and stir vigorously.

2. Set a video camera running or assign some children to photograph the mixture at (say) 30-second intervals.

3. While waiting for the soil to settle, discuss with the children what is in the soil. Ask: *Where does it come from, and what properties does it have?*

4. Either looking at the actual mixture, or at the video or photographs, as the different components of the soil settle, ask children what they notice, and why they think this is happening. (Essentially, the separation of the different elements is by weight, the moving water keeping the lighter particles suspended for longer.)

Independent work
5. Give each child photocopiable page 75 'Separating solids' and ask them to complete it.

Differentiation
● Support children through further discussion and demonstration of the diagrams on the photocopiable sheet, allowing them to discuss the events, then complete the work together.
● Challenge children to research the exact meaning of sedimentation, and to find two or three different ways that it is used in industry.

Science in the wider world
In industry, sedimentation techniques are used in the manufacture of liquids such as alcohol and fuel. Once the solid elements have settled, the clean liquid is drawn off, or in reverse, such as making paper where the liquid drains away to leave the pulped wood, or in food manufacture to remove debris.

Review
Ask the children to work in small groups and compare their work, prompting them to check that they have spotted the basic difference in the order that the materials finish. Come together and discuss the pros and cons of each approach (sieving is cleaner, but using water requires minimal equipment). To conclude, explain to the children how water filtration plants work: basically, for part of the process dirty water is passed through beds of different sized particles so that impurities may be filtered out. This obviously has to be done on a very large scale to provide clean tap water for us all.

Objectives
● To understand that when some mixtures mix with water some of their components may dissolve.
● To identify substances which are soluble and insoluble in water.

Resources
Soil; sieves; gravel; glass beaker; sand; salt; sugar; water; photocopiable page 76 'Investigating mixtures'; mixing jars; stirrers; filter paper; funnels; collecting jars; a video or digital camera (optional)

Speaking scientifically
dissolve, insoluble, soluble, solution

Lesson 3: Investigating dissolving

Introduction

Take a small amount of soil and pour it through a set of sieves. Half fill a small glass beaker with water and add some soil and stir well. Finally, take the beaker of soil and water and pour it through a funnel containing filter paper and collect the run-off in a jar. As you work, explain what is happening and reinforce vocabulary. Discuss the contents of the filter paper and the jar, and discuss their state. Ask: *Is the water in the jar as clean as it was before the soil was mixed with it? Is the soil the same as it was beforehand?* Elicit that soil does not dissolve in water, and that filter paper is like a very fine sieve.

Ideally, film the following experiment close up, and then show it to the children on your whiteboard.

Paired or group work

1. Distribute photocopiable page 76 'Investigating mixtures'. Explain that the children are to work systematically to complete the chart for all of the materials shown. Tell them it is advisable to do 'dry' sieve work before 'wet' filtering work to allow for easy materials re-use, although the order of material mixing is up to them, depending on how they divide roles in their group.

2. Briefly touch on roles in the group, discussing different ways of dividing up tasks whilst ensuring that all group members understand the outcomes. Discuss also what the groups will need to do to ensure that the experiment is fair and meaningful.

3. Write an 'equipment and materials' list on your whiteboard, and ask the children to collate all of the equipment and materials they need. Before they start work remind them that they do not need to mix large quantities of each substance to perform their experiments.

> **Differentiation**
> ● Group children appropriately and guide them in task distribution, with good writers recording results, for example, while others observe the experiments.

Science in the wider world

Filters for cleaning air and water are used a lot in the home, for example, in vacuum cleaners, tumble driers and washing machines. These become ineffective after a while and need regular cleaning.

Review

Gather the children and discuss results systematically, checking for incorrect observations or discrepancies between groups. If the children do not use the language themselves, introduce the terms *dissolve, insoluble, soluble* and *solution*, and use them in the context of discussing their findings. To conclude, ask: *Imagine that all of the substances that we have investigated were mixed together with some soil. What would be the most effective way to remove them from the soil?*

Objectives
● To know that evaporation can be used as a means of recovering a dissolved solid.

Resources
Water, glass or plastic Petri dishes; table salt; Epsom salts; sugar; measuring spoons; black paper; magnifying glasses; digital camera (optional); interactive activity 'Investigating evaporation'

Speaking scientifically
crystals, dissolve, evaporate, insoluble, soluble, solute, solution, solvent

Lesson 1: Investigating evaporation

Introduction

Write the words *evaporate*, *solute*, *solution* and *solvent* on the board, and ask the children to write down each word and its definition alongside it. After a few minutes confirm the correct definitions:

- evaporate: to turn from liquid into vapour
- solute: a substance that is dissolved in another substance
- solution: a liquid mixture which has had something dissolved in it
- solvent: a substance that something is dissolved in.

Alternatively, use the media resource 'Investigating evaporation' on the CD-ROM to discuss the definitions as a class. Recap these terms in the context of the previous lessons, naming examples of solutes and solvents.

Whole-class work

1. Set up and carry out tests for different solutes that dissolve in water. Measure out three equal quantities of water, and add around a teaspoon of salt, Epsom salt and sugar into each. Stir the solutions until the solutes have all dissolved, then pour a good quantity of each into separate Petri dishes or shallow glass containers. (It may be wise to have a second set of three dishes of the solutions, and place them out of reach as a backup.)

2. Putting black paper under each one, place them in a location in the classroom where they will be undisturbed, but also where it is not too cool. Ideally, next to the dishes, have a *diary* available that can be completed once an hour to monitor the progress of each, as well as a digital camera for recording.

3. Ask the children to monitor the progress of each dish until all of the water has evaporated, photographing the final crystals.

Independent work

4. Ask the children to write up the results of the evaporation tests, structuring their work appropriately, using diagrams and images, and concluding their piece with an explanation for what they have observed. Remind the children that they must include information about where the water has gone, and what changes they notice in the solutes.

Differentiation
● Support children by providing a structured writing frame, or a cloze text, focusing on the words *solution*, *evaporation*, *vapour* and *crystals*.
● Challenge children by asking them to speculate on why the different crystals have formed in the shapes they have, and provide enlarged sketches of each type.

Science in the wider world

Seawater is salty because of the salts in rocks which have dissolved and been washed into the sea over millions of years. Rain water is not salty because the salt doesn't evaporate with the water from the sea in the water cycle.

Review

Look at the diary and any photographs taken, and consider what took place from the moment the solutions were prepared. Use magnifying glasses or macro photographs to look at the crystals in detail, considering features and differences. Ask the children to explain what has happened, verifying correct responses and correcting misconceptions.

Objectives
● To learn how mixing, dissolving, filtering and evaporating can be used in separating materials.

Resources
Sand; salt; mixing jars and stirrers; tweezers; measuring spoons; scales; heating sources (if possible); sieves; water; filter paper; funnels; collecting jars; Petri dishes

Speaking scientifically
dissolve, evaporate, filter, insoluble, soluble, solution

Lesson 2: Separating sand and salt

Introduction

Ask for two volunteers to take part in a contest and divide the children in two halves to support each volunteer. Next, mix two small piles of salt and sand in jars or on paper. Give each volunteer a pair of tweezers and ask them to race to see who will be the first to separate the two substances in their pile.

Consider their achievements after two minutes. How much did they separate, and how 'pure' are their separated piles? Consider the reasons why separating these substance 'physically' is so difficult.

Group work

1. With everyone watching, mix 50g each of salt and sand together. Explain that the children will be working in groups to separate the two substances as effectively as possible. Point out that the two separated piles they create will be weighed at the end to see how closely they match the original weights.

2. Show the children the equipment and materials available and ask them to work together in their groups to create a written plan to explain how they will separate the two substances.

3. Make sure that they discuss the essential points needed in their plans:
- the sequence of actions proposed
- the equipment needed
- why they are choosing their approach
- what they expect to happen.

4. Once a group has agreed that their plan is appropriate, and you have checked it, they can collect their equipment and carry out their plan.

Differentiation
● Support some children by allowing them to contribute orally, and by providing as much opportunity as possible for them to observe the experiments.
● Challenge some children by introducing a three-substance mixture using sand, salt and iron filings (children must be closely supervised at all times if handling iron filings).

Science in the wider world

After salt has been extracted from seawater or mines, purification techniques (such as filtering) are needed, as there will often be impurities in the salt that are not suitable for consumption.

Review

The review session may need to be done on a separate occasion if you are waiting for water to evaporate. Ask each group to bring their two materials to the front for the weigh-in. It may be that the weights are actually greater than first measured if the substances are still wet. Discuss this and consider options. Highlight any different approaches taken by groups, and consider actions that were particularly effective, as well as those that didn't work.

Finally, ask each group to give their two substances a purity rating, asking: *How alike are the separated substances to their original state?*

Objectives
● To demonstrate knowledge of reversible changes.

Resources
Trilby; dark glasses (optional); secondary sources on different scientific areas to those covered in this chapter; some equipment and materials already used in this chapter

Speaking scientifically
All scientific language introduced in this chapter can potentially be used

Lesson 3: Scientific detective manuals

Introduction

If possible, start the lesson in role as a detective. Explain that as a detective you constantly need to update your knowledge and skills. Say that orders have come in from your superiors that you are now the Head Spy for Materials and their Properties (HSMP). You must improve your understanding of substances immediately, so that you can catch criminals, solve crimes and find stolen goods. In particular you want to learn how to separate substances, and how to reverse changes in materials.

And what luck! You have heard that this very class has a great deal of scientific knowledge. You would therefore like them to prepare a manual of information, explanations and tips that will help you in your work.

Group work

1. Arrange the children in groups of three to six, and show them a range of information books. Discuss text layout, style, images, and so on, and consider what would be useful for the detective manual. For example:

- concise, clear information with diagrams where needed
- real-life application
- additional facts
- a glossary of terms.

2. Discuss the information that might be included, creating a list on your whiteboard for everyone to see. For example:

- separating solids from solids
- separating solids from liquids
- separating dissolved solids (including how to speed this up)
- porous materials and removing air.

3. Focusing on one of these elements, briefly recap the work done in class, modelling good vocabulary and naming equipment used. Discuss why a detective might want to know this information, and list one or more of the possible real-life criminal uses of the science: dissolving substances in water to smuggle them; mixing gold dust with gravel to hide it; analysing which pen was used to write a ransom note; separating a non-dissolvable powder from sugar; and so on.

4. This task can easily be extended to cover more than one lesson if high-production standards are expected.

Differentiation
● Before the children start working encourage groups to allocate roles and tasks accordingly. They might just produce a page each, or some children might focus on diagrams while others write explanations. Whatever they decide, ask them to plan thoroughly before they start their work.
● Challenge children to use ICT to research and/or present the manual in order to provide a greater range of skill-development.

Science in the wider world

Although this lesson is a fun way for children to re-present their knowledge and understanding, it is also worthwhile pondering on how science truly affects the world of crime and crime-busters. People do try to smuggle things like drugs and diamonds mixed in with other substances, and detectives really do analyse evidence to match it to suspects and their possessions.

Review

With yourself back in role, encourage each group to present its manual, allowing children time to consider each other's work. Make a great show of appreciation and reinforce good language and knowledge as you explain how their information and recommendations will be useful to you.

Objectives
● To compare and group together everyday materials based on evidence from comparative and fair tests.

Resources
Photocopiable page 'Uses of everyday materials' from the CD-ROM; pencils; paper

Working scientifically
● Presenting findings in written form, displays and other presentations.

Uses of everyday materials

Revise
● Talk to the children about some of the properties of the materials around the classroom and the school. Ask: *Why are specific materials used and not others?* For example:
- Why are the windows made of glass?
- What are the properties of glass that make it good for windows?
- Why isn't your coat made from tissue paper?
- What properties does the material that makes your coat have to have?
- Why don't you wear iron gloves? What about wooden ones?

● Talk to the children about the materials that absorb water and why they need to be absorbent. (For example, paper towels are made of loose-weaved paper made of tiny openings.) Remind them that it is capillary action that allows the water to move up into a material such as a paper towel. Ask them what happened when they put polythene under a piece of cotton and then dripped water on to it. What happened when they rubbed wax on to cotton and then dripped water on to it?

Assess
● Give children photocopiable page 'Uses of everyday materials' and ask them to complete it.

Further practice
● If you think that the children need to explore different materials in more detail, look again at buildings. Use the school (kitchens are full of machines and cooking utensils) or any unusual ones in the local neighbourhood. Ask: *Why is this specific material being used and not something else?*

Objectives
● To compare and group together everyday materials based on evidence from comparative and fair tests, including their conductivity and response to magnets.

Resources
Photocopiable page 'Conductors and insulators' from the CD-ROM; materials that will and will not conduct electricity; materials such as metal sheets; metal and wooden spoons; polystyrene; wool; foam; thin card; foil; paper fasteners

Working scientifically
● Presenting findings in written form, displays and other presentations.

Conductors and insulators

Revise
● Hold up a selection of different materials and ask the children whether they think they are conductors of electricity or insulators. (They should know without having to test them.) Remind them that insulators prevent the electrical current from flowing and conductors allow the current to flow. Show them sheets of metal and metal spoons, together with wooden spoons and a piece of polystyrene and a woollen jumper. Ask the children which materials are good thermal conductors.

Assess
● Give the children photocopiable page 'Conductors and insulators' and ask them to complete it.

Further practice
● The children could use their knowledge of conductors and insulators to make switches in an electrical circuit.

Objectives
● To use knowledge of solids, liquids and gases to decide how mixtures might be separated, including through filtering, sieving and evaporating.

Resources
Photocopiable page 'Separating substances' from the CD-ROM

Working scientifically
● Identifying scientific evidence that has been used to support or refute ideas or arguments.

Separating substances

Revise
● Recap on key vocabulary for states of matter and the interactions between different substances: air, chromatography, dissolve, evaporate, filter, gas, insoluble, liquid, molecule, particle, porous, sieve, soil, solid, soluble, solute, solution, solvent, steam, vapour. Be sure to reinforce the associated vocabulary with the properties of different states of matter.
● Create a labelled display of all the equipment used over the course of this chapter.
● Discuss everyday instances and equipment where substances are separated, such as a cafetière for separating coffee grinds, or a colander for removing water.
● Reinforce children's appreciation of on-going evaporation by drawing chalk lines around rainwater puddles, tracking their progress as they disappear.
● Review any videos of experiments to consolidate pupils' memories of the equipment and processes involved.

Assess
● In assessing children's written work, look for awareness of chemical properties and processes in different experiments: their awareness of substances' hardness, shape, solubility, and even chemical composition.
● In listening to children's talk, discussions and responses, look for those using appropriate vocabulary to describe chemical processes, the equipment used and procedures for separating materials.
● Use photocopiable page 'Separating substances' to formally assess children's knowledge and understanding of separating materials.

Further practice
● Try to introduce new materials for children to suggest separation techniques, such as getting the nuts out of a bar of chocolate, trying chromatography with plants, or capturing the gas from fizzy drinks.
● Review children's *Detective manuals*, and consider what would need to be added to them to make them into survival guides for, say, a trip to the rainforest.

ΦSCHOLASTIC

Name: _____   Date: _____

The shaky-hand machine

■ You will need:

bare wire   a small buzzer
insulated   sticky tape
electrical wire   modelling dough
9v battery

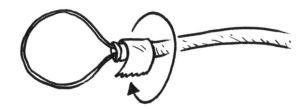

■ Bend a length of wire into a loop about the size of a 10p coin and attach it to a length of electrical wire using sticky tape.

■ Bend another piece of wire into a series of curves, making sure that they do not touch each other. Remember, the more bends you have the harder the game!

■ Put the bendy wire through the loop and stick one end into modelling dough and attach the other end to one terminal of the buzzer.

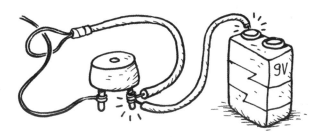

■ Now attach the electrical wire to the other terminal of the buzzer and one terminal of the battery.

■ Use another piece of wire to connect the battery and buzzer.

■ Now you are ready to see who has the shakiest hands!

I can create a simple electrical circuit.

How did you do?

Name: _____

Date: _____

Making it flow

■ Which materials conduct electricity (that is, let if flow through them)? Carry out this investigation to find out.

You will need: a battery, a bulb in a holder, some wires with crocodile connectors.

1. Make an electrical circuit to light a bulb, as shown below.

2. Now add an extra crocodile connector wire to your circuit.

1

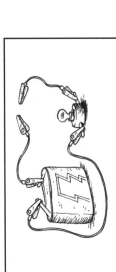

2

3. Collect some things made with different materials; for example: aluminium foil, string, polythene, and iron key, a brass screw, an elestic band, a plastic pen top, water, a coin, stainless steel, wood, a wire pipe cleaner or pencil 'lead'⁓⁓⁓⁓⁓⁓⁓⁓ .

string   elastic band   plastic pen top   water

stainless steel   wire pipe cleaner   pencil lead

4. Clip each of these things in turn between the crocodile connectors. Does the electricity still flow to the bulb?

5. Complete this table to record your results.

Object	Made of:	Conducts electricity?

■ What do you notice about the things that conduct electricity?

PHOTOCOPIABLE

Name: _____ Date: _____

Travelling heat

You will need: a pencil; a collection of objects to test; supervised access to a hot radiator or sunny window sill; a freezer.

Heat is always trying to escape. It travels from hot spots to colder areas. Heat can travel through some materials more quickly than others.

■ Collect these objects for the tests.

a piece of card   something plastic
a cork   a metal object
a piece of fabric   a piece of
something wooden   polystyrene

■ Find out which materials heat can travel through quickly. Use the chart to write down your results.
■ First, feel each object and decide whether it is hot, warm, cool or cold.
■ Put the object in a warm place such as on a radiator or a sunny window sill.
■ After ten minutes, touch each object carefully and decide if there is any change.
■ Put the same objects in a freezer for ten minutes.
■ Quickly decided how they feel.

Name of object	How it felt			X ✓
	before the test	after being in a hot place	after being in a freezer	

■ Put a tick next to the objects which quickly changed their temperature.
■ Put a cross next to the objects which hardly changed.

✓ These materials let heat pass through them easily. They are good conductors of heat.	X These materials did not let heat pass through them easily. They are good insulators of heat.

I can explain which materials are good conductors of heat.

How did you do?

Magnetic forces

You will need: two bar magnets, the objects listed below.

■ Which of these things will be attracted to a magnet?
Predict first, then use your magnet to see if you were right.

■ Record your results on the chart below.

Object	Prediction	Result
2p coin		
10p coin		
ruler		
eraser		
nail		
paper		
paper-clip		
plastic lid		
glass jar		
pin		
pencil		
elastic band		

■ Discuss your results with a friend. What materials do you think are magnetic?

When two magnets pull towards each other, they are said to attract.
When two magnets push each other away, they are said to repel each other.

■ Find out what happens when you try each of these:

Two North poles adjacent:
repel or attract? _____

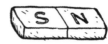 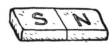

North and South poles adjacent:
repel or attract? _____

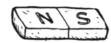 

South and North poles adjacent:
repel or attract? _____

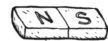 

Two South poles adjacent:
repel or attract? _____

■ Summarise what you have discovered by completing this sentence:

Unlike poles _____, whereas like poles _____.

I can tell which materials are attracted or repelled by magnets.

How did you do?

PHOTOCOPIABLE

SCHOLASTIC
www.scholastic.co.uk

Name: _____   Date: _____

Useful plastic

You will need: a collection of plastic items; some of the same items in different materials; a pencil; paper.

There are about 30 different types of plastic in general use.

■ Collect ten plastic items that you use every day. Examine them carefully and tick their properties in this table.

Name of item	thin	firm	transparent	can be folded	light in weight	waterproof	breakable	long-lasting

Now find two items, one made of plastic and the other made of a different material, which both have the same use, like the examples below:

plastic and wooden clothes pegs
plastic and metal spoons
plastic and glass jugs

■ Compare the two items, writing down the good points and bad points of each. Getting rid of plastic can be difficult. Rubbish is often buried.

■ Bury some different types of plastic in the ground together with some pieces of paper and wood. Examine them every week and record what happens to them.

I can identify the properties of different types of plastic.

How did you do?

Investigating porosity

■ Use the charts below to investigate how porous different materials are.

Stones

	Jug readings in millilitres		Volume of water/air in sample
	Start	Finish	Start – finish
Test 1			
Test 2			
Average of test 1 and 2			

Gravel

	Jug readings in millilitres		Volume of water/air in sample
	Start	Finish	Start – finish
Test 1			
Test 2			
Average of test 1 and 2			

Sand

	Jug readings in millilitres		Volume of water/air in sample
	Start	Finish	Start – finish
Test 1			
Test 2			
Average of test 1 and 2			

Conclusion _____

_____

I can use water to find out how porous something is.

How did you do?

PHOTOCOPIABLE   **SCHOLASTIC** www.scholastic.co.uk

Separating solids

- A class do two different experiments using a mixture of stones, gravel and sand.
- Label the diagrams to show how the experiments finished, and explain each one.

Pour mixture through a set of sieves:

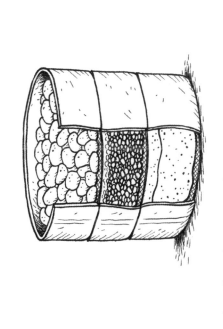

Explain what has happened.

_____

_____

Mix and stir in a jar with water:

Explain what has happened.

_____

_____

What are the advantages of each method? _____

_____

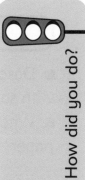

How did you do?

I can explain how different sized particles form different layers.

PHOTOCOPIABLE

Name: _____ Date: _____

Investigating mixtures

■ Describe what you see when you mix each of the following, first with soil and then with soil and water.

■ What does it show when you filter each one, first with sieves and then with filter paper?

	Gravel	Salt	Sand	Sugar
1. Mixed with soil				
2. Poured through sieves				

	Gravel	Salt	Sand	Sugar
1. Mixed with soil and water				
2. Poured through filter paper				

What conclusions can you draw?

_____

_____

I can describe what happens when some substances are mixed with water and say why.

How did you do?

PHOTOCOPIABLE

www.scholastic.co.uk

Earth and space

Expected prior learning
- Observe the apparent movement of the Sun during the day.
- Observe and describe weather associated with changes across the four seasons and how day length varies.
- Explain that we see things because light travels from them to our eyes.
- Associate shadows with a light source being blocked by something; find patterns that determine the size of shadows.
- Some forces need contact between two objects and some act at a distance.

Overview of progression
- Explain the rotation and orbit of the Earth creating days and years.
- Explain seasons caused by the Earth's tilt on its own axis and orbit of the Sun.
- Study the movement of the Earth/Moon relative to the Sun in the solar system.
- Study the phases of the Moon.
- Study the arrangement of the planets in the solar system.
- Investigate the development of theories relating to the arrangement of stars and planets in the universe.

Creative context
- This topic provides many opportunities for the children to make observational drawings and use graphs to present their findings.
- The children will be required to deploy their D&T skills to make models of the solar system.
- There are opportunities for the children to improve their speaking and presentation skills towards the end of the unit while studying scientists.

Background knowledge
A day is the length of time it takes for a planet to rotate once on its own axis. A year is the length of time it takes for a planet to orbit the Sun once. The Earth is tilted on its own axis and this causes the seasons. When the northern hemisphere is tilted towards the Sun it will be summer in the northern hemisphere; when it is tilted away from the Sun it will be winter. The Moon orbits the Earth. It takes 28 days for the Moon to complete one orbit. The reflection of the Sun from the surface of the Moon and the changing position of the Moon causes the phases of the Moon. The planets in the solar system all orbit the Sun. Several of them have moons that orbit them. At one time scientists thought that the Sun and all the planets in the solar system orbited the Earth. Copernicus and Galileo discovered that all the planets orbit the Sun.

Speaking scientifically
- The children will need to know the words describing the movement of the Earth and the Moon. They will also need to know the names of the planets in the solar system and be introduced to the terms *geocentric solar system* (where the Earth is at its centre) and *heliocentric solar system* (where the Sun is at its centre) in order to understand how scientists' view of the solar system has changed.

Preparation
Week 2, lesson 1 requires children to contact friends or relatives living in other time zones to confirm the time there. Warn the children in advance that they are going to be completing this activity, so that they can contact their friends and relatives abroad and ask them to be available at the time of the lesson.

You will need to provide: Resources are listed for every lesson. You will also need a globe, internet access, toy model people, a torch and bright lamp.

On the CD-ROM you will find: photocopiable pages 'Map of the world', 'Labelled time zones', 'How the Moon formed', 'Ptolemy and Alhazen', 'Copernicus and Galileo', 'Brahe, Kepler and Newton', 'Phases of the Moon', 'The moons of Jupiter'; interactive activities 'Day and night', 'Phases of the Moon', 'Ordering planets', 'The seasons', 'Famous scientists and evidence'

Chapter at a glance

Week	Lesson	Curriculum objectives	Lesson objectives	Main activity	Working scientifically
1	1	• (Y3) To recognise that they need light in order to see things and that dark is the absence of light.	• To recall that we see things because light travels to our eyes. • To recall objects that are light sources. • To recall knowledge of the Sun and stars as sources of light. • To consider existing knowledge of space.	Classifying objects as light sources.	• *Using relevant scientific language and illustrations to discuss, communicate and justify their scientific ideas.*
	2	• To describe the Sun, Earth and Moon as approximately spherical bodies.	• To understand how we know that the Earth is spherical. • To know the sizes of the Earth, Moon and Sun and the distances between them.	Discovering the Earth is round by using secondary sources. Comparing the sizes of the three spheres – the Earth, the Moon and the Sun.	• Identifying scientific evidence that has been used to support or refute ideas or arguments.
	3	• To use the idea of the Earth's rotation to explain day and night and the apparent movement of the Sun across the sky.	• To understand that the Earth rotates. • To know the movement of the Sun across the sky. • To understand how the Earth's rotation relates to the measurement of time.	Making a sundial in the classroom. Demonstrating the Earth's rotation on its axis and how this causes day and night.	• Using simple models to describe scientific ideas. • Taking measurements, using a range of scientific equipment, with increasing accuracy and precision taking repeat readings when appropriate. • Recording data and results of increasing complexity.
2	1	• To use the idea of the Earth's rotation to explain day and night and the apparent movement of the Sun across the sky.	• To know that there are different time zones. • To understand that time zones relate to the position of the Sun in the sky.	Examining the time zones on a world map. Using the internet to confirm the time in places in different time zones. Communicating with friends or relatives in different time zones to confirm the time.	• *Recognising which secondary sources will be most useful to research their ideas.*
	2	• To use the idea of the Earth's rotation to explain day and night and the apparent movement of the Sun across the sky.	• To understand that planets rotate on their own axes. • To understand that the length of a day relates to a planet's rotation.	Researching day length for other planets in the solar system.	• Recording data and results of increasing complexity using scientific diagrams and labels, classification keys, tables, scatter graphs, bar and line graphs.
	3	• To describe the movement of the Earth, and other planets, relative to the Sun in the solar system.	• To know how the Earth moves around the Sun. • To understand that the length of a year relates to a planet's orbit around the Sun.	Modelling the movement of the Earth around the Sun. Researching year length for other planets in the solar system.	• Using simple models to describe scientific ideas.
3	1	• To describe the movement of the Earth, and other planets, relative to the Sun in the solar system.	• To understand that the change in sunrise times is related to the angle of tilt and the Earth's position on its orbit.	Plotting given times of sunrise through the year on a graph and relating it to the position of the Earth in orbit.	• Recording data and results of increasing complexity using scientific diagrams and labels, classification keys, tables, scatter graphs, bar and line graphs. • Reporting and presenting findings from enquiries.
	2	• To describe the movement of the Earth, and other planets, relative to the Sun in the solar system.	• To understand that the seasons are related to the angle of tilt and the Earth's position on its orbit.	Demonstrating the Earth's orbit of the Sun and relating the seasonal variations to the position of the Earth in its orbit.	• Reporting and presenting findings from enquiries.
	3	• To describe the movement of the Moon relative to the Earth.	• To discover how the phases of the Moon occur.	Shining a light on a ball to demonstrate the phases of the Moon and its orbit around the Earth.	• Using simple models to describe scientific ideas.

SCHOLASTIC

Chapter at a glance

Week	Lesson	Curriculum objectives	Lesson objectives	Main activity	Working scientifically
4	1	• To describe the movement of the Moon relative to the Earth.	• To know that an object moving in front of a light produces a shadow. • To know that a solar eclipse is a shadow caused by the Moon. • To know that the Earth turning makes the shadow seem to move.	Modelling a solar eclipse.	• Using simple models to describe scientific ideas.
	2	• To learn that the Sun is a star at the centre of the solar system and has eight planets.	• To know the positions of the planets in the solar system. • To know what the planets in the solar system are like.	Producing travel brochures describing the conditions on other planets.	• Recognising which secondary sources will be most useful to research their ideas.
	3	• To learn that the Sun is a star at the centre of the solar system and has eight planets.	• To know the positions of the planets in the solar system. • To understand that as the Earth moves around the Sun, the Moon also moves around the Earth.	Modelling the structure of the Solar System. Producing a mobile of the solar system.	• Using simple models to describe scientific ideas.
5	1	• To understand that a moon is a celestial body that orbits a planet.	• To understand how moons are believed to have formed. • To know the planets that have moons.	Finding out about the formation of moons – Earth's big splash, Jupiter's gravity and captured asteroids.	• Reporting and presenting findings from enquiries.
	2	• To learn that the Sun is a star at the centre of our solar system.	• To understand why some stars are brighter than others. • To understand the arrangement of stars in constellations.	Finding out about the brightness of stars and how they form constellations.	• Using simple models to describe scientific ideas.
	3	• To learn that the Sun is a star at the centre of our solar system.	• To understand how scientists look for planets around other stars. • To understand that the Sun is a star in a galaxy. • To understand the relationship of galaxies to the universe.	Explaining how scientists identify planets in other solar systems and how they try to identify planets where life could be sustained.	• Reporting and presenting findings from enquiries.
6	1	• To consider the work of scientists such as Ptolemy and Alhazen.	• To learn about Alhazen's work on how we see objects. • To understand Ptolemy's idea of the geocentric solar system. • To understand that the idea had flaws and there were attempts to correct them.	Researching the life and work of Ptolemy and Alhazen. Considering the insistence of Alhazen of explaining phenomena using knowledge and not ideas.	• Identifying scientific evidence that has been used to support or refute ideas or arguments. • Reporting and presenting findings from enquiries.
	2	• To consider the work of scientists such as Copernicus and Galileo.	• To understand the life and work of Copernicus. • To understand the life and work of Galileo.	Discovering the development of the heliocentric solar system, the work of Copernicus and the work of Galileo on astronomy.	• Identifying scientific evidence that has been used to support or refute ideas or arguments. • Reporting and presenting findings from enquiries.
	3	• To consider the work of scientists such as Brahe, Kepler and Newton.	• To understand the life and work of Brahe, Kepler and Newton.	Discovering the work of Brahe and Kepler and the work of Newton on motion and the law of gravitation.	• Identifying scientific evidence that has been used to support or refute ideas or arguments.
Assess and review					

Objectives
● To recall that we see things because light travels to our eyes.
● To recall objects that are light sources.
● To recall knowledge of the Sun and stars as sources of light.
● To consider existing knowledge of space.

Resources
A suitable video clip of a rocket launch; a variety of objects that are light sources (candle, torch, mobile phone, lamp, digital alarm clock); a variety of objects that are not light sources including some shiny objects (mirror, pencil, mug, exercise book, magazine)

Speaking scientifically
space, Earth, Moon, Sun, light, gravity, reflection, light source

Lesson 1: What do we know about space?

Previous knowledge
The children should have studied the apparent movement of the Sun and the creation of shadows as well as sources of light and how we see.

Introduction
Find a suitable video clip on the internet of a rocket/shuttle launch. Show it to the children. Ask them where they think the rocket is travelling. Elicit that it is travelling into space, possibly to the Moon or one of the planets in the solar system. Ask the children if they were on the spaceship, what objects they would expect to see out of the window on their journey. List these on the board (and leave this on the board until later in the lesson). This part of the lesson could be extended if you want. Ask the children to describe or write down how they think they would be feeling if they were on the spaceship as it took off and what they would want to have with them if they were going to undertake such a journey.

Whole-class work
1. Shine a torch at the class. Ask the children how they are able to see the torch. Explain that light is travelling from the torch to the eye, and that this is how we are able to see the object.

2. Hold up an object that is not a light source, such as a pencil case, and ask the children how they are able to see this object. Explain that while the torch produced its own light that travelled to the eye, we can see other objects because they reflect light that travels to the eye. Explain that some objects are light sources while others reflect light so that we can see them.

Paired work
3. Place different objects around the room and ask the children to look at each one and classify it as *a light source* or *not a light source*.

4. Tell them to record their results in a suitable table.

Independent work
5. Draw the children's attention to the list of objects on the board of things that might be found in space. Ask the children to classify these as *light sources* or *not light sources*. Emphasise again that only some objects are light sources and that we can see other objects in space because they reflect light.

Introducing the new area of study
Ask the children to name as many objects as they can in space. Write these in two lists on the board, without explaining the criteria that you are using. The first column is objects in the solar system, the second, objects that are not in the solar system. Ask the children if they can explain why they have been grouped as they have. Elicit that the first column is a list of objects in the solar system. Explain that this is a group of planets that orbit the Sun and that this makes up a very small part of space.

Differentiation
● Support children during the practical activity to classify objects as light sources.
● Challenge children to explain why the planets in our solar system stay in orbit around the Sun.

Science in the wider world
Space travel is a much-explored topic in both fiction and non-fiction and people are fascinated by the objects that can be found in space and the possibility of life on other planets.

Checkpoint
● Can the children identify sources of light?
● Do they know that we see things because light travels to our eyes?
● Do they recognise the Sun as a light source?
● Can they distinguish between sources of light and reflective objects?

Review

Go through the children's tables together and check that they have correctly identified the sources of light. Talk about the shiny objects to ensure that children understand that these are only shiny because they reflect light.

Objectives
● To understand how we know that the Earth is spherical.
● To know the sizes of the Earth, Moon and Sun and the relative distances between them.

Resources
Footballs/tennis balls/table tennis balls (one of each per group); two large pieces of card; two small model people; photocopiable page 102 'Round Earth or flat Earth?'; photographs of the Earth seen from space; model of the solar system (optional)

Speaking scientifically
Sun, Moon, Earth, spherical, star

Lesson 2: The shape of the Sun, Earth and Moon

Introduction

Ask the children what shape the Earth is and establish that it is spherical. Ask them what evidence they have for this and then show them photos of the Earth taken from space as evidence. Point out that these are relatively recent and ask what people thought the shape of the Earth was before there was photographic evidence. Elicit that people have thought the Earth was spherical for several hundred years, but that before this they believed that the Earth was flat.

Whole-class work

1. Make a 'flat' and 'round' Earth model. On each, in turn, place two model people near one edge of the 'land', then move one away and ask what the person left behind will see as the other retreats. Establish that on the 'flat' Earth the person just gets smaller and smaller whereas on the 'round' Earth, the figure disappears feet first.

2. Explain that in ancient Greece, philosophers observed that:

● ships sailing away from all known ports 'disappear' hull-first, just as if they are sailing over a hill;
● during lunar eclipses, the Earth's shadow on the Moon always appears circular and the only shape that always casts a circular shadow is a sphere.

Independent work

3. Give out photocopiable page 102 'Round Earth or Flat Earth?' and ask the children to complete it.

Group/Whole-class work

4. Ask the children to use the internet to research the size of the Sun, Earth and Moon and then write them in order according to their size.

5. Pull together as a class and discuss their findings. Explain that even though the Moon looks bigger in the sky than the Sun it only appears this way because it is so much closer. (Remind children that they should never look directly at the Sun.)

> **Differentiation**
> ● Support children by showing them a scale model of the solar system to emphasise this point.
> ● Challenge children to find out more about the discoveries that led to the knowledge that the Earth is round and/or to draw a scale model of the Sun, Moon and Earth and distances between them.

Science in the wider world

Understanding that the Earth is spherical is crucial to understanding how day and night occur, how seasons happen, and why some places on Earth are always hot, while others are always cold.

Review

Using the balls, ask the children to decide which ball should represent the Sun, the Earth and the Moon. Ask them to position each ball to represent the relative distance between the three bodies.

Objectives
- To understand that the Earth rotates.
- To know the movement of the Sun across the sky.
- To understand how the Earth's rotation relates to the measurement of time.

Resources
Modelling dough; pencils; A3 paper; torches; rulers; a globe; Blu-Tack® and three or four model/toy people; photocopiable page 103 'Shadows'; photocopiable page 104 'Crossword puzzle'; blinds or curtains drawn in the classroom if available

Speaking scientifically
shadow, sunrise, sunset, midday, rotation, axis, spin

Lesson 3: Shadows

Introduction
Check that the children know how shadows change throughout the day, and that this change occurs because the Sun appears to move across the sky. Establish that shadows are shortest at midday, when the Sun is highest in the sky. Discuss where the Sun rises and sets and the position of the Sun in the sky at different times of the year.

Group work
1. Ask the children to place a piece of modelling dough in the middle of a piece of A3 paper and stick a pencil upright into it. They should then use the torch to model the Sun moving across the sky.

2. Ask them to measure the length of the shadow at *different times of the day* – ensuring that the torch models the position of the Sun at that time.

3. Ask the children to create a line graph recording the length of shadow against time of day. They should conclude that shadows are shortest in the middle of the day and longest at sunrise and sunset.

Independent work
4. Give out copies of photocopiable page 103 'Shadows' and ask the children to complete it.

Whole-class work
5. Establish with the class that although the Sun appears to move across the sky during the day, the Sun does not actually move; the Earth is in fact rotating on its own axis and this causes this effect.

6. Using one of the torches and the globe, demonstrate how the Earth spins on its own axis anticlockwise, as seen from the top, and how this gives rise to day and night, and the apparent movement of the Sun across the sky during the day.

7. Attach toy people to the globe in different places and rotate the globe, encouraging the children to say the time of day or night for each of the models.

Differentiation
- Support children by demonstrating the practical activity to them rather than them completing it themselves.
- Challenge children to explain why shadows are much shorter at the equator.

Science in the wider world
For centuries sundials have been used to tell the time. However, in order to tell the correct time sundials must be aligned with the axis of the Earth's rotation.

Review
Ask the children to complete photocopiable page 104 'Crossword puzzle'. (The answers are: 1. night-time; 2. shadow; 3. longer; 4. morning; 5. rotate; 6. daytime; 7. facing; 8. noon; 9. dusk; 10. spherical. The shaded word is *twenty-four*, which is the answer to a question such as *How many hours are there in a day?*)

Objectives
● To know that there are different time zones.
● To understand that time zones relate to the position of the Sun in the sky.

Resources
Interactive activity 'Day and night' on the CD-ROM; a globe; Blu-Tack® and three or four model/toy people; photocopiable page 105 'Time zones'; access to the internet, email or Skype; photocopiable page 'Labelled time zones' from the CD-ROM

Speaking scientifically
time zone, rotation

Lesson 1: Time zones

Introduction
Complete the interactive activity 'Day and night' on the CD-ROM with the class. Repeat and recap the activity from the last lesson looking at how the Earth's rotation gives rise to day and night. Ask the children about the time of day the different model people on the globe would be experiencing. Ask: *If it's midday for this person, what time would it be for a person on the opposite side of the world?* Introduce the idea of time zones and explain that different time zones are used in different countries so that everyone experiences appropriate times for the position of the Sun in the sky.

Paired work
1. Give the children photocopiable page 105 'Time zones' and ask them to use the internet to allocate times to the different time zones.

Group work
2. Ask the children to email or Skype friends and relatives abroad to confirm that the time zones on their sheets are accurate.

Differentiation
● Support children to understand time zones and how all time zones are referenced to Greenwich Mean Time.
● Challenge children to tell you the time in different countries of the world at different times in London.

Science in the wider world
China and India are both very large countries that have decided to have only one time zone. This means that, in China, solar 'noon' can happen as late as 15.00 in some parts of the country.

Review
Photocopiable page 'Labelled time zones' from the CD-ROM with the time zones marked on it. Go through this with the class. Explain that all times are referenced to the time at Greenwich in London, hence Greenwich Mean Time (GMT) and that if you go to Greenwich you can see the line that represents Greenwich Mean Time. Ask any group who has managed to contact friends and relatives abroad to show the class where they have contacted. Calculate with the class what the time should be in that location and then ask the group to confirm.

Objectives
- To understand that planets rotate on their own axes.
- To understand that the length of a day relates to a planet's rotation.

Resources
A globe; access to the internet; graph paper

Speaking scientifically
day (defined as the time taken for a planet to spin once on it's own axis), solar system, axis

Lesson 2: Planet days

Introduction
Ask: *What is a 'day'?* Ask the children to think about it on their own before comparing their definition with that of another child, and then, as a pair, with another pair in order to write a definition between the four of them. Take some of the definitions from the class and then recap using the globe to ensure that all the children correctly understand the definition of the term *day* (the time taken for the Earth to spin on its own axis once). Explain the distinction between the everyday and scientific meanings of the word *day*.

Whole-class work
1. Ask the children to name any of the other planets in the solar system. Write a list on the board and then order them so that they are in order of distance from the Sun (Mercury, Venus, Earth, Mars, Jupiter, Saturn, Uranus and Neptune).

2. Ask the children if they think that the length of a day would be the same on each of these planets. Elicit that different planets take different amounts of time to spin on their own axis and therefore each of the planets in the solar system has a different day length.

3. Ask: *Which planet do you think will have the longest day length?* Write their suggestions on the board to return to later.

Paired work
4. Allow the children to use the internet to find the day length for each of the planets in the solar system, recording their results in a suitable table.

Differentiation
- Support children by providing them with the day length for some of the planets to cut down on the amount of research they have to do.
- Challenge the children to find out the size of each of the planets and conclude if there is a relationship between size of planet and day length.

Science in the wider world
Day is defined as the time it takes for a planet to rotate on its own axis once. This is different for each of the planets in the solar system and so each of the planets have very different day lengths.

Review
Compare the children's results with their initial suggestions. Ask: *Is there any relationship between day length and distance from the Sun?* (No, it relates to the speed that the planet rotates.)

Lesson 3: Planet years

Introduction
Ask: *What time unit is defined by the movement of the Earth?* (a day, a year) Explain that months are measured by the movement of the Moon, but that a year is defined by the movement of the Earth. Ask: *Which movement of the Earth is defined as a year?* Elicit that as well as spinning on its own axis (*day*), the Earth also orbits around the Sun; the time taken for the Earth to orbit the Sun once is defined as a *year*.

Whole-class work
1. Demonstrate how years occur by placing the lamp in the centre of the room to model the Sun, and then moving the globe around the 'Sun' several times. Ask the children to call out when each year has been completed (at the end of one complete orbit).

2. Explain that the time taken for the Earth to orbit isn't exactly 365 days (a calendar year) but actually a little longer (365¼ days) and that is why we have a leap year every four years in order to keep the times correct.

Paired work
3. Ask the children to recall the list of planets in the solar system from the previous lesson. List these on the board and ask the children if they think that all of the planets take the same time to orbit the Sun and hence have the same year length.

4. Discuss with the children whether there is a relationship between the distance from the Sun and orbit time.

5. Ask the children to research the orbit times of the planets in the solar system, recording their data in a suitable table.

> ### Differentiation
> ● Support children to explain how the movement of the Earth causes a day and a year by giving them a cloze activity to complete.
> ● Challenge the children to plot a graph of orbit time against the distance from the Sun and to draw a conclusion as to whether there is a relationship or not.

Science in the wider world
A year is defined as the time taken for a planet to orbit the Sun. Year length varies for different planets

Review
Ask pairs to present their tables. Conclude that, in general, the further the planet is from the Sun, the longer the time taken to orbit, and the longer a year is in length.

Objectives
● To understand that the change in sunrise times is related to the angle of tilt and the Earth's position on its orbit.

Resources
A globe; graph paper; a lamp; photocopiable page 106 'Sunrise and sunset'

Speaking scientifically
winter, summer, seasons, tilt, orbit

Introduction
Ask the children to write a paragraph describing a winter's day and then a summer's day. Get some of the children to read out what they have written. Ask the children what the main differences are between winter and summer days. Elicit that in summer the days are longer, and the nights shorter and it is warmer. In winter the days are shorter, the nights longer and it is colder.

Independent work

Month	Jan	Feb	Mar	Apr	May	Jun
Sunrise time	7.59	7.14	6.14	6.05	5.09	4.43
Sunset time	16.21	17.16	18.05	19.58	20.46	21.20
Month	Jul	Aug	Sep	Oct	Nov	Dec
Sunrise time	5.01	5.46	6.35	7.25	7.19	8.00
Sunset time	21.11	20.23	19.15	18.07	16.11	15.52

1. Give the children the above data and ask them to show the information as a bar graph. The times shown are the average times for the month.

Whole-class work
2. Discuss the findings from the children's graphs (days are longer in summer and shorter in winter).

3. Place the lamp in the centre of the room to represent the Sun. Using the globe, show the orbit of the Earth around the Sun. Show the children how the Earth is tilted on its own axis and how this makes the northern hemisphere closer to the Sun for half of the year and further away from the Sun for the other half of the year.

4. Explain that when the northern hemisphere is closer to the Sun, day lengths are longer and that when the northern hemisphere is pointing away from the Sun, day lengths are shorter.

Independent work
5. Ask the children to complete photocopiable page 106 'Sunrise and sunset'.

Differentiation
● Support children by giving them prepared axes on which to plot separate bar charts of the sunrise and sunset times to the nearest half hour.
● Challenge children to decide what type of graph they should plot with the data they are given.

Science in the wider world
Day length changes throughout the year. This is because the Earth is tilted on its own axis and as it orbits the Sun the northern and southern hemispheres are relatively closer to and further from the Sun.

Review
Ask the children to explain in their own words how day length changes during the year and explain why it changes. Ask the children to read out their accounts, and help them to improve what they have written.

Objectives
● To understand that the seasons are related to the angle of tilt and the Earth's position on its orbit.

Resources
A globe; a torch; a lamp; photocopiable page 107 'The seasons'; interactive activity 'The seasons' on the CD-ROM

Speaking scientifically
seasons

Lesson 2: Seasons

Introduction
Ask the children if they can explain in their own words why the length of day varies from summer to winter. In order to consolidate understanding of this difficult concept, repeat the demonstration from the previous lesson showing the Earth's orbit around the Sun and how the tilt on its own axis makes the northern hemisphere closer to the Sun for half of the year (and hence gives longer days) and further away from the Sun for the other half of the year (giving shorter days).

Whole-class work
I. Replace the lamp with a child holding a torch to represent the Sun. This time, as the Earth completes its orbit, ask the children to describe where it will be hot, and where it will be cold.

2. Show them the area covered by a torch beam shone at different places on the globe. Explain that when the northern hemisphere is in the part of the Earth's orbit where it is tilted away from the Sun, then the increased distance from the Sun and the Sun's rays being spread over a larger area both make the temperature colder. When the northern hemisphere is tilted towards the Sun, it is closer and the Sun's rays are concentrated in a smaller area, making this part of the Earth warmer.

3. Ask the children to complete photocopiable page 107 'The seasons'. The answers are as follows: 1. The northern hemisphere should point towards the Sun; 2. The correct sentences are: The South Pole is in constant darkness; The North Pole is in constant daylight; Sunlight reaching Britain is spread over a small area; 3. As the Earth orbits the Sun, the Northern hemisphere gradually moves until it is tilting away from the Sun. When this happens, the Sun's radiation is spread over a larger area, making it cold. This is winter. The Earth has to move 180° around its orbit for the change from summer to winter to take place. This takes six months, as the entire orbit takes a year.

Differentiation
● Support children to explain how temperature and day length vary throughout the year by asking them to produce a poster showing how the seasons are different.
● Challenge children to come to the front and explain to the rest of the class why day length and temperature vary throughout the year. You can use interactive activity 'The seasons' on the CD-ROM to go over some key points.

Science in the wider world
The seasons happen because the Earth orbits the Sun and is tilted relative to the plane of its orbit. The tilt of the Earth means that the northern hemisphere is sometimes tilted towards the Sun and sometimes tilted away from the Sun, depending on where the Earth is in its orbit. Summer in the northern hemisphere occurs when it is tilted towards the Sun, winter when it is tilted away from the Sun.

Review
Ask the children to produce a piece of creative writing explaining what life would be like if something happened to the Earth so it was no longer tilted on its own axis. Their writing should reflect the fact that there would be no seasons and the weather and day length would be constant throughout the year.

Lesson 3: Phases of the Moon

Objectives
● To understand how the phases of the Moon occur.
● To understand that as the Earth moves around the Sun, the Moon also moves around the Earth.

Resources
A football painted half black and half white (do not use a balloon); a lamp; images from the internet of the phases of the Moon in the correct order; interactive activity 'Phases of the Moon' on the CD-ROM; picture cards showing the phases of the Moon

Speaking scientifically
Moon, phases, full moon, crescent, waxing, waning, half moon

Introduction
Ask the children if anyone can explain the significance of a month as a length of time. Elicit that a month is the amount of time that it takes for the Moon to orbit the Earth once. Ask the children to describe the Moon as they have seen it in the sky and discuss the fact that the Moon appears to change shape as the month progresses. Ask the children to describe the shapes of the moon that they have seen and then project an image from the internet of the phases of the Moon in the correct order.

Whole-class work
1. Tell the children they are going to model how the Moon can look different at different times.

2. Place a reading lamp on one side of the classroom (the Sun). Hold up a football (the Moon). Ask: *What would this look like in bright Sunlight?* Make sure the children understand that it will always be half light and half dark.

3. Hold the ball so that the white side points to the *Sun*. Sit the children as shown in the diagram below and stand in the position marked 'M'. Ask: *What does the 'Moon' look like?* (a full Moon) and then: *Where can the Moon go, so that it looks all black?*

4. Help the children to discover that it must be between them and the Sun (this is a new Moon). Ask the children to suggest how they think the *Moon* might be moving? (It moves in an orbit around the Earth.) Orbit around the children so that they can see the phases of the *Moon*.

5. Repeat the orbit a few times until all the children are confident about which phase of the Moon they see in each position of the *Moon's* orbit.

Independent work
6. Ask the children to complete the interactive activity 'Phases of the Moon' on the CD-ROM.

> ### Differentiation
> ● Support children by giving them a worksheet showing most of the phases of the moon with a few gaps for the children to fill in, rather than the suggested review activity.
> ● Challenge children to come to the front and explain to the rest of the class how the phases of the moon occur.

Science in the wider world
The side of the Moon that is never seen is referred to as the dark side of the Moon. As you have to travel into space to see this side of the moon only a very few people have ever seen it in anything other than photographs.

Review
Give the children a set of cards showing the phases of the Moon. Ask them to place them in the correct order.

Objectives
• To know that an object moving in front of a light produces a shadow.
• To know that a solar eclipse is a shadow caused by the Moon.
• To know that the Earth turning makes the shadow seem to move.

Resources
Video of a solar eclipse; a bright lamp; a cardboard circle fastened to a thin stick to represent the Moon

Speaking scientifically
light, shadow, Moon, Earth, solar eclipse

Lesson 1: Solar eclipse

Introduction
Show the children a video of a solar eclipse, and discuss what they see, concentrating on what it is that moves in front of the Sun (the Moon), and the fact that it goes dark during an eclipse because the Moon is creating a shadow. Tell the children that they are going to model a solar eclipse to see if they can explain exactly what is happening.

Whole-class work
1. Show the children the lamp and the cardboard circle and tell them that they represent the Sun and the Moon. Show them how moving the *Moon* in front of the *Sun* casts a shadow on the wall. Once the children have seen how the *Moon* casts a shadow, line up half the class along the wall, with the other half behind the *Sun* to watch.

2. Move the *Moon* gradually across in front of the *Sun*. Ask the children who are standing against the wall to describe what they see as the *Moon* passes in front of the *Sun*. Swap over the two groups of children and repeat.

3. Help the children to share their observations from both positions to realise that as the shadow passes over them, against the wall, they become unable to see the *Sun*, just as in a real solar eclipse.

4. Encourage the children to remember what happens to ordinary shadows formed by the Sun throughout the day, and help them to deduce from this that the reason the Moon's shadow moves across the Earth is because the Earth is turning on its own axis, not because the Sun is moving, and that this explains why a solar eclipse never lasts long in one place.

Group work
5. Write the following information on the board about solar eclipses: *A solar eclipse occurs when the Moon goes in front of the Sun and blocks most of the Sun's light from the Earth. During a total eclipse all you can see from the Earth is a ring of light around the Moon which is part of the Sun the Moon did not cover.* Ask the children to draw a series of diagrams to explain this.

Differentiation
• Support children by giving them a pre-prepared diagram showing what happens during a solar eclipse. They can use the information on the board to label the diagram.
• Challenge children to draw a series of diagrams to explain what happens during a solar eclipse without giving them any additional information.

Science in the wider world
Primitive people in ancient times thought that eclipses meant that something terrible was about to happen, because the sky gets unnaturally dark; the Sun can disappear for minutes at a time during these events.

Review
Ask the children to imagine that they were present during a real solar eclipse. They should use what they have learned from the video to write a postcard to a friend, describing what the eclipse was like.

Objectives
● To know the positions of the planets in the solar system.
● To know what the planets in the solar system are like.

Resources
Access to the internet; secondary sources on the planets in the solar system; travel brochures; interactive activity 'Ordering planets' on the CD-ROM

Speaking scientifically
solar system, planets, Moon, Mercury, Venus, Earth, Mars, Jupiter, Saturn, Uranus, Neptune, mnemonic

Lesson 2: The planets of the solar system (1)

Introduction
Ask the children to name the planets in the solar system. (Pluto has been reclassified and is no longer considered to be a planet and so the eight planets in the solar system are: Mercury, Venus, Earth, Mars, Jupiter, Saturn, Uranus, and Neptune.) Write these on the board in order of distance from the Sun or use interactive activity 'Ordering planets' on the CD-ROM. Ask the children to come up with a mnemonic to help them remember the order, for example: *My Vicious Earthworm Might Just Swallow Us Now.* Ask some of the children to share their mnemonics with the rest of the group.

Group/paired work
1. Tell the children that they are going to produce a travel brochure for one of the planets in the solar system. Ask them to suggest what information should be included in the brochure (distance from the Sun; number of moons; day length; length of year; average temperature; minimum and maximum temperatures).

2. Record these ideas on the board so that the children can refer to them during the activity. You may also wish to discuss the layout of the brochure with the children or allow them to look at some travel brochures to see what they look like.

3. Allow the children time to use the internet and other secondary sources to research their chosen planet before they produce their brochures.

> ### Differentiation
> ● Support children by giving them a writing grid within which they can record the information about the planet they choose to research.
> ● Challenge children to research a planet that is not in the solar system and produce a travel brochure for that planet.

Science in the wider world
The idea of space travel fascinates people and we move closer to space tourism all the time. Whilst people are unlikely to travel to other planets for a holiday, the Virgin Galactic project is currently building a commercial spaceport in New Mexico in order to allow people to pay to travel into space. It is now possible to reserve places on their *SpaceShipTwo!*

Review
Ask the children to tell the rest of the class about their travel brochure and why people should buy a holiday to their planet.

Objectives
● To know the positions of the planets in the solar system.
● To understand that as the Earth moves around the Sun, the Moon also moves around the Earth.

Resources
Named cardboard disks to represent each planet coloured appropriately; two more disks with *Moon* and *Sun* written on them coloured appropriately; string or thread; coloured paper and card; sticky tape; strips of wood or coat hangers to use as the hanger for the mobile

Speaking scientifically
solar system, planets, Moon, Mercury, Venus, Earth, Mars, Jupiter, Saturn, Uranus, Neptune

Lesson 3: The planets of the solar system (2)

Introduction

Ask one child to hold the *Sun* disk and ask them to stand in the middle of the room. Ask the children how the Earth moves around the Sun. Give a volunteer the *Earth* disk and ask them to show how it orbits the Sun. Ask for further volunteers to show how the other planets orbit the Sun. As each planet is added into the role-play check that they are in the correct order from the Sun. Emphasise the speed at which each planet orbits the Sun – the further from the Sun, the longer the planet will take to complete its orbit. Finally, give a child the *Moon* disk and ask them to show how the Moon orbits the Earth. Emphasise that all the planets in the solar system orbit the Sun but the Moon only orbits the Earth (although other planets have their own moons).

Group work

1. Ensure that the children know the names of all the planets in the solar system and their order from the Sun. Ask them to produce a mobile showing all the planets and the Sun in the solar system.

> ### Differentiation
> ● Support the children by helping them to get their planets in the right order in their mobile.
> ● Challenge one of the children in the group to organise the role-play in the introduction part of the lesson.
> ● Challenge the children to produce a mobile where the planet sizes and distances apart are to scale.

Science in the wider world

Scientists have only recently been able to detect planets orbiting stars in other parts of the universe, in effect, other solar systems. The planets become detectable because of the effect that they have on the star that they orbit, which is detected by incredibly sensitive apparatus.

Review

Ask the children to use their knowledge from the previous two lessons to write three facts about the planets in the solar system; two true facts and one false fact. They can then test their facts on other children (or even the whole class) to see whether they can spot the *fib*!

Objectives
● To understand how moons are believed to have formed.
● To know the planets that have moons.

Resources
A set of cards (see right for details); access to the internet; photocopiable page 'How the Moon formed' from the CD-ROM

Speaking scientifically
moon, satellite, orbit

Lesson 1: Other moons

Introduction

Produce a set of cards with the names of the planets in the solar system and their main moons (see information below). Ask the children to try to match each of the planets with their moon. (They should know at least some of these from their travel brochure work in week 4 lesson 2.) Go through this with the class and ensure that they have the correct answers.

Earth	Moon
Jupiter	Io
Saturn	Titan
Neptune	Triton
Mars	Phobos

Whole-class work

1. Ask the children how moons are different to planets. Elicit that the planets in the solar system orbit the Sun, whilst a moon orbits a planet.

2. Explain that moons are thought to have formed by:

● accretion – where the moon forms from clumps of matter such as gas and dust that orbit the parent planet. Most of the regular moons are thought to have formed this way, including the Earth's moon which is thought to have formed from debris that was knocked off the Earth when a large planet collided with it early on its history.

● capture – where space debris passed close enough to a planet to be *captured* by its gravity. Many of these orbits are wide and eccentric, and on an entirely different plane to that of the planets, and hence is how most of the irregular moons came to be.

Group work

3. Give the children photocopiable page 'How the Moon formed' from the CD-ROM for them to complete.

> **Differentiation**
> ● Support children by giving them the sentences describing how moons form but with key words missing. The children can then fill in the missing words.
> ● Challenge the children to do their own research and explain to the rest of the class how moons form.

Science in the wider world

There is actually no strict definition of what a moon is, but there are some commonalities between those objects considered to be moons, also called satellites. They all are:

● distinct, whole objects
● solid objects
● in orbit around a more massive body (that orbits a star).

Moons however, come in all shapes and sizes. We tend to think of objects like our Moon, that are large and round, but moons like Phobos and Deimos (the moons of Mars) look more like small irregularly-shaped asteroids.

Review

Reissue the cards from the introduction. This time ask the children to place them face down on the desk and play a game of matching pairs, turning over two cards at a time and keeping the correct pairs. The child with the highest number of matching pairs at the end is the winner.

Objectives
● To understand why some stars are brighter than others.
● To understand the arrangement of stars in constellations.

Resources
Photocopiable page 108 'Star patterns' cut up into individual cards; secondary sources on constellations or access to the internet; a room with blinds or curtains; black card; torches; modelling clay, tools for making holes (bradawls)

Speaking scientifically
star, constellation

Lesson 2: Stars

Introduction
Discuss the children's experiences of seeing stars in the night sky. Explain that stars are like the Sun in that they are balls of fire that give out light (and so are light sources), but as they are further away from the Sun they look smaller. Explain that in this activity they will be seeing why some stars appear to be bigger and brighter than others.

Group work
1. Ask the children to make some different-sized holes in a piece of black card, showing them how to make a hole safely by pushing the bradawl through the card into the modelling clay.

2. Ask the children to shine their torches through the cards and experiment with moving nearer and further from each other to explore how this changes what they can see.

3. Establish that the brightness of the torch and the size of the hole will both affect the apparent brightness of the star. Explain that in the sky, the size and brightness of the star, as well as its distance from the observer, will affect how it looks.

Paired work
4. Ask the children if they have ever seen patterns of stars in the sky. Explain that when we look at the night sky we can see groups of stars arranged in patterns. In the ancient past, people have imagined that these look a bit like a person or an animal and have given them special names.

5. Ask the children to use secondary sources and the internet to name as many of the star constellations on photocopiable page 108 'Star patterns' as they can.

Differentiation
● Support children by drawing in the lines on the constellations to make the patterns more obvious.
● Challenge children to find out about the North Star and to mark it onto the appropriate constellation (the Big Dipper).

Science in the wider world
In ancient times, before the discovery of the compass, stars were used by sailors for navigation.

Review
Ask the children to explain why some stars appear bigger and brighter than others. Finally, ask them to explain why the Sun is so bright. (Remind children never to look directly at the Sun.)

Objectives
• To understand how scientists look for planets around other stars.
• To understand that the Sun is a star in a galaxy.
• To understand the relationship of galaxies to the universe.

Resources
Set of cards with the following words on them: *Moon, Earth, Sun, solar system, galaxy, universe*; photographs of the Moon, Earth, Sun, solar system, galaxy and universe

Speaking scientifically
solar system, galaxy, universe

Lesson 3: The Sun is a star at the centre of our solar system

Introduction
Ask the children to put the cards in size order starting with the smallest first. Go through the correct answers with the children, showing them images of each object as you do so. Explain that the planets of the solar system are a very small part of a larger body called the Milky Way (our galaxy) and that the Milky Way is a small part of the universe.

Whole-class work
1. Explain that there are other *solar systems* within our galaxy and within other galaxies where a group of planets are orbiting a massive object such as a star.

2. Also explain that scientists study these planets to see if any of them have conditions similar to those on the Earth such as conditions that are *just right* to support life.

3. Ask the children how scientists determine whether something is alive or not. Remind them that living things all have to do the following: move, excrete, reproduce, respire, respond to stimuli, need nutrition, and grow in order to be considered to be *alive* and that any organisms found on other planets would have to fulfil these criteria in order to be considered to be living.

Independent work
4. Ask the children to imagine that they are planning to travel to a planet in another solar system. Ask them to describe their journey from the moment they leave Earth in their spaceship, to arriving at the new planet and what they find there.

Differentiation
• Support children to help them work out the relative size of the Sun, the solar system, a galaxy and the universe.
• Challenge children to do further research into how scientists look for planets around other stars, including how planets around other stars make them wobble and blink.

Science in the wider world
Observatories are always placed in areas of low population density because there is far less light pollution there. Some observatories have been launched into space to measure light from stars; scientists look for the tiny dimming of light caused by a planet passing in front of one of the stars, blocking some of the starlight from reaching the space observatory.

Review
Ask the children to read out some of their accounts of travelling to another planet. If they claim to have encountered alien life ask them how they determined that the things they encountered were alive. Ask the children to write their full address starting with street and house number, going onto country, continent, planet, solar system, galaxy and universe.

Objectives
● To learn about Alhazen's work on how we see objects.
● To understand Ptolemy's idea of the geocentric solar system.
● To understand that the idea had flaws and there were attempts to correct them.

Resources
Poster-making materials; photocopiable page 'Ptolemy and Alhazen' from the CD-ROM

Speaking scientifically
geocentric solar system

Lesson 1: Ptolemy and Alhazen

Introduction
Hold up an object so that the class can see it and ask the children, working in pairs, to discuss how we are able to see the object. Take feedback from the children and elicit that we can see the object because light reflects off it into our eyes (this is revision of the first lesson in this chapter).

Whole-class work
1. Ask the children if they think that people have always thought that this is how we are able to see objects. After discussion, explain that before we knew this people thought that we could see things because light travels from our eye to the object we are looking at. However, through experimentation, a scientist called Alhazen came up with a different theory.

2. Read the information about Alhazen on the photocopiable page 'Ptolemy and Alhazen' from the CD-ROM. Explain that this is how science works. Scientists look at evidence, and then develop a theory about how something works.

3. Ask the children if they think that people have always known that the Earth orbits the Sun or if at one time people might have had other ideas. Discuss, and explain that at one time people firmly believed that the Earth was the centre of the universe, and the Sun and the other planets in the solar system orbited the Earth.

4. Explain that Ptolemy was the scientist who proposed this idea (known as the geocentric solar system) and tell them something about Ptolemy and his work (see photocopiable page 'Ptolemy and Alhazen' from the CD-ROM for more information).

Paired work
5. Ask the children to produce a poster showing what Ptolemy thought the solar system looked like.

> **Differentiation**
> ● Support children by providing them with information about the work of Ptolemy so that they can produce a poster.
> ● Challenge children to do their own research to find out about Ptolemy.

Science in the wider world
Alhazen's use of observation and experience rather than logic and theory to support or refute ideas and arguments changed the way scientists work. Scientists today would always draw conclusions from experimental evidence or look for evidence to support their ideas before presenting them to the science community.

Review
Ask the children to present their posters to the rest of the class.

Objectives
● To understand the life and work of Copernicus.
● To understand the life and work of Galileo.

Resources
Access to the internet; photocopiable page 'Copernicus and Galileo' from the CD-ROM

Speaking scientifically
geocentric, heliocentric, Copernicus, telescope, Galileo

Lesson 2: Copernicus and Galileo

Introduction
Read and discuss together the photocopiable page 'Copernicus and Galileo' from the CD-ROM. Explain that in addition to these discoveries, Galileo also discovered that everything falls at the same speed. He dropped two round balls off the Leaning Tower of Pisa. One was very heavy, and one was light. Both hit the ground at the same time. However, the most important thing about Galileo is that he was not guessing. He provided proof that what he had discovered was true.

Group work
1. Place the children into groups of three or four. Ask them to imagine that they are living in the time of Copernicus and Galileo. The work of these two scientists has just been announced. Their task is to produce a news report for the local radio station on the recent discoveries.

Differentiation
● Support the children by ensuring that they are in a mixed ability group and so will be able to progress with the work.
● Support the children by giving them a number of sentences about the work of Galileo and Copernicus to put in order rather than giving them the research and radio report activity.

Science in the wider world
New scientific discoveries today are very dependent on providing evidence. This evidence needs to be very robust as it will be checked and tested very thoroughly by other scientists before new theories and ideas are accepted.

Review
Ask the children to present their radio reports to the rest of the class.

Objectives
● To understand the life and work of Brahe, Kepler and Newton.

Resources
Photocopiable page 'Brahe, Kepler and Newton' from the CD-ROM; photocopiable page 109 'Earth and space'; interactive activity 'Famous scientists and evidence' on the CD-ROM

Speaking scientifically
ellipse, orbit, gravity

Lesson 3: Brahe, Kepler and Newton

Introduction
Have a question and answer session covering the work of Ptolemy, Alhazan, Copernicus and Galileo. For example, ask: *What did Ptolemy think the Universe looked like? What did Copernicus invent?*

Whole-class/independent/group work/paired work
1. Introduce the work of the three scientists Brahe, Kepler and Newton and read through the information on photocopiable page 'Brahe, Kepler and Newton' from the CD-ROM.

Group work
2. Working in groups of three or four, ask the children to produce a mini play outlining the work of Brahe, Kepler and Newton.

> ### Differentiation
> ● Support children by giving them information about the three scientists from which they can produce a play.
> ● Challenge children to do their own research into the discoveries by these three scientists before producing their play. You can use the interactive activity 'Famous scientists and evidence' on the CD-ROM to go over some key points about the scientists discussed.

Science in the wider world
Scientists very often work collaboratively or even correctly interpret others' data when the collector of the data has not been able to. The work of Brahe and Kepler illustrates this very well.

Review
Ask the children to complete photocopiable page 109 'Earth and space'.

Objectives
● To use the idea of the Earth's rotation to explain day and night.
● To describe the movement of the Earth relative to the Sun in the solar system.
● To describe the movement of the Moon relative to the Earth.

Resources
A globe; bright lamp; table tennis ball; access to computers to produce PowerPoint presentations; a torch

Working scientifically
● Presenting findings in written form, displays and other presentations.

Days, years, months and seasons

Revise

● Using the lamp and the globe, demonstrate how the Earth spins on its own axis and how this gives rise to day and night. Rotate the globe and ask the children to give the approximate time of day or night for different parts of the Earth.

● Define a *day* as the time it takes for the Earth to spin on its own axis once. Show the children how the Earth orbits the Sun and remind them that the length of time taken for the Earth to orbit the Sun once is a year.

● Show the children how the Earth is tilted on its axis and ask the children what effect this has. (It causes the seasons.) Show the children how, as the Earth orbits, the northern hemisphere is first closer to the Sun, causing summer – longer days and higher temperatures, but then how six months later, as it orbits, the northern hemisphere is further from the Sun, causing winter – short days and lower temperatures.

● Use the torch to show how in the hemisphere that is tilted away from the Sun, the Sun's rays are spread out more over the Earth's surface and explain that this is part of the reason why the temperature is lower. Finally, use the tennis ball to model the Moon and show how this obits the Earth once every 28 days and remind the children that this length of time is approximately one month.

Assess

● Ask the children to produce a PowerPoint presentation. Their presentation needs to be four slides long and contain the following information:
  ● Slide 1: explain what causes day and night
  ● Slide 2: explain what causes a year
  ● Slide 3: explain what causes the season to happen
  ● Slide 4: explain what causes months.

● The children can complete their PowerPoint presentations in groups of two or three. They can then present them to the rest of the class.

Further practice

● Ask the children to explain as part of their PowerPoint presentation why day-lengths do not vary at all if you live on the equator, whereas they can be very short or very long if you live within the Arctic Circle.

Objectives
- To observe and name a variety of sources of light.
- To describe the movement of the Moon relative to the Earth.
- To use simple models to describe scientific ideas.

Resources
A football painted half black and half white (not a balloon); a lamp; photocopiable page 'Phases of the Moon' from the CD-ROM

Working scientifically
- Presenting findings in written form, displays and other presentations.

Phases of the Moon

Revise

- Ask the children how it is possible for us to see objects in space. Elicit that while some objects (such as stars) we can see because they emit light, other objects (such as planets and moons) we can see because they reflect light from the Sun.
- Repeat the role-play exercise from week 3, lesson 3, modelling how the Moon looks at different times. Repeat the orbit a few times until all the children are confident about which phase of the Moon they see in each position of the *Moon's* orbit.

Assess

- Ask the children to complete photocopiable page 'Phases of the Moon' from the CD-ROM. The answers are 1. New Moon; 2. Half Moon; 3 See diagram; 4. The Earth has to turn a bit further before the Moon comes into view, so the Moon will rise later.

Further practice

- Place the children into groups and give each group a half black, half white football and a lamp and ask them to create their own modelling role-play of the phases of the Moon.

Objectives
● To know that the Sun is a star at the centre of the solar system and has eight planets that orbit it.
● To know that a moon is a celestial body that orbits a planet.

Resources
Image of Jupiter and its moons to project to the whole class; photocopiable page 'The moons of Jupiter' from the CD-ROM; poster making materials

Working scientifically
● Presenting findings in written form, displays and other presentations.

The moons of Jupiter

Revise
● Remind the children of their work on the solar system and the order of the planets in the solar system from the Sun. Listen to one or two of the mnemonics that they wrote earlier in the chapter to help them remember the order of the planets.
● Ask the children which of the planets has the longest orbit around the Sun. Elicit that the further a planet/moon is from the object it is orbiting the longer its orbit will take. Remind the children that some of the planets in the solar system have moons and reissue the cards from week 5, lesson 1 of the planets in the solar system and their moons.
● Ask the children to pair up the cards. (If any of the children produced a travel brochure for holidays to Jupiter in week 4, lesson 2 then show them to the class to emphasise that Jupiter has many moons.) Show the children an image of Jupiter and its moons. Briefly discuss how moons form around planets and why they stay in orbit around their planet (see week 5, lesson 1).

Assess
● Introduce photocopiable page 'The moons of Jupiter' from the CD-ROM and explain to the children that for this assessment they have to draw a poster showing the moons of Jupiter and label it to show their understanding of this part of the topic.

Further practice
● Remind the children of the terms geocentric and heliocentric. Challenge the children to explain on their posters how Galileo used the four moons of Jupiter to show that the solar system is heliocentric rather than geocentric.

Round Earth or flat Earth?

■ Draw three pictures to show what an observer on land would see as a ship sails further and further away.

■ If the world is flat.

■ If the world is round.

■ As a ship approaches land anywhere in the world, the sails come into view first. What does this tell you about the shape of the Earth?

_____

■ Colour in blue the stars that observer A would be unable to see. Colour in red the stars that observer B would be unable to see. Explain to a friend what observer C notices about the stars she can see as she walks from A to B.

I can make observations about land, seas and the skies based on my knowledge the Earth.

How did you do?

PHOTOCOPIABLE   **SCHOLASTIC**
www.scholastic.co.uk

Shadows

■ These children measured a shadow at different times of the day.

Length of shadow (cm)

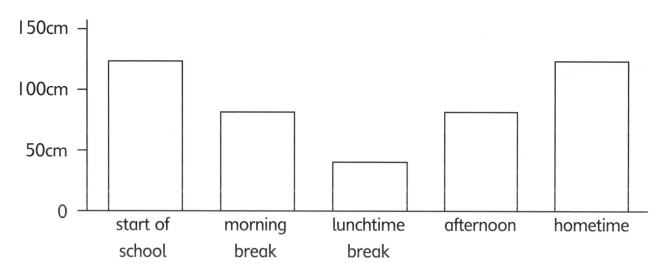

■ How many times did the children go and measure the shadow? _____

■ When was the shadow the shortest? _____

■ How long was the shadow at morning break? _____

■ Estimate how long the shadow was at breakfast time. _____

■ Describe what happened to the length of the shadow. _____

_____

I can understand why shadows change during the day.

How did you do?

Crossword puzzle

■ Fill in the answers to the clues. Make up a question about the Earth with the answer that you find in the shaded squares.

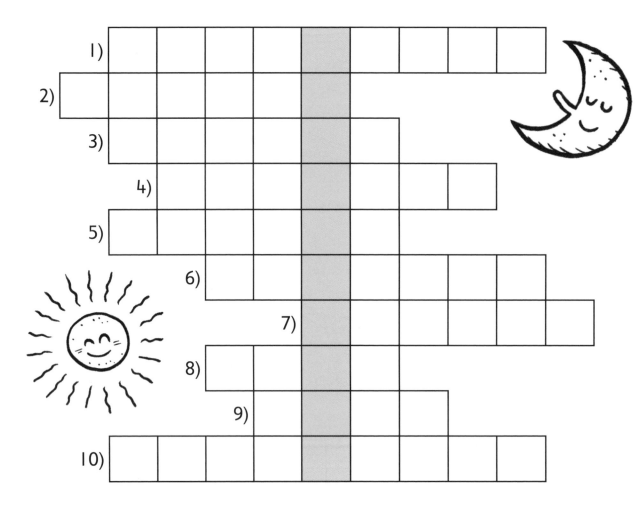

1. It is this time when you cannot see the Sun.

2. A stick in sunshine will have one of these.

3. As the afternoon passes, shadows will get _____.

4. The time when shadows are gradually getting shorter.

5. The Earth does this once every day.

6. It is this time when you can see the Sun in the sky.

7. Cold places are _____ away from the Sun.

8. This is the time when shadows are shortest.

9. This is the time when the Sun disappears below the horizon at the end of the day.

10. The Earth is approximately this shape.

I can answer questions on the subject of Earth and space.

How did you do?

Name: _____   Date: _____

Time zones

■ Use the internet to allocate times to the different time zones.

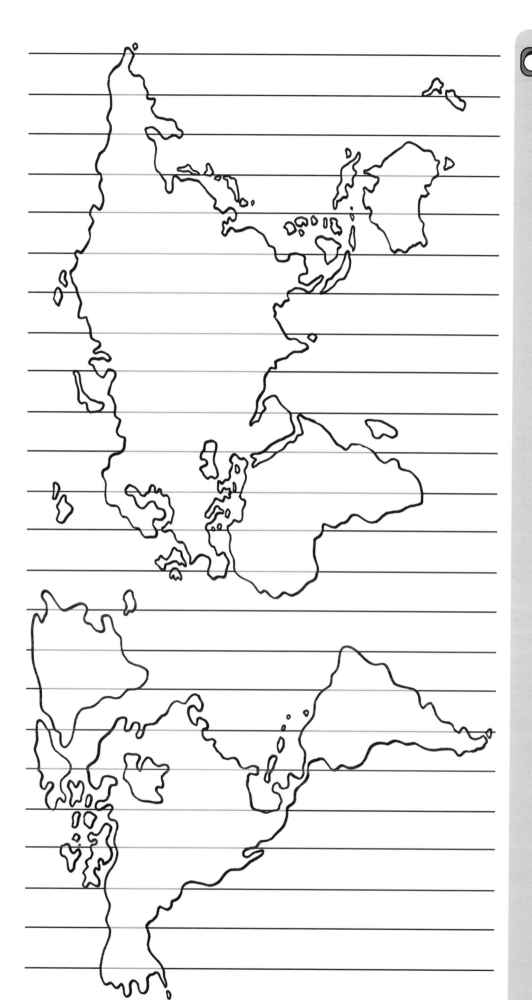

I can say what time it is in different parts of the world.

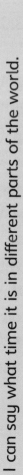

How did you do?

Name: _____   Date: _____

Sunrise and sunset

- The graph below shows the time that the Sun rises on the first day of each month throughout the year.
- The jumps on 1 April and 1 October show when daylight-saving time begins and ends. The dotted line shows the time when the Sun would have risen without daylight-saving time.

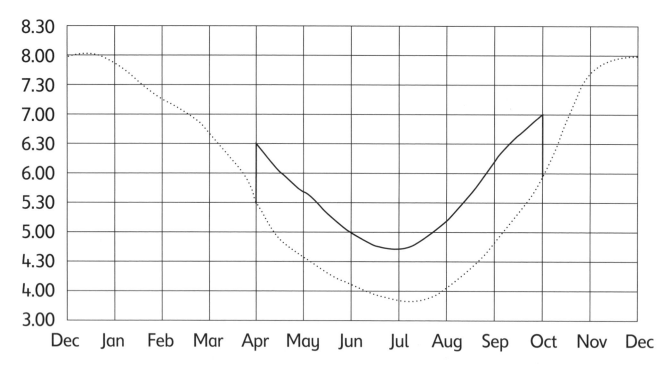

- What time does the Sun rise on 1 March? _____.
- What is the earliest time the Sun rises? _____.
- When does this happen? _____.
- What is the difference between the earliest sunrise time and the latest sunrise time? _____.
- What time does the Sun rise on 1 May? _____.
- What time would it have risen on 1 May without daylight-saving time? _____.
- What effect does daylight-saving time have on how light it is early in the morning? _____.
- Draw a line to show how the graph would look if the sunrise times were all an hour later. Ignore daylight-saving time. _____.

I can use a graph to work out what time the Sun rises and sets on certain dates.

How did you do?

PHOTOCOPIABLE   **SCHOLASTIC**
www.scholastic.co.uk

Name: _____   Date: _____

The seasons

■ Draw a diagram of the Earth and Sun to show the position that the Earth will be in when it is summer in Britain.

■ Some of the sentences below are correct when it is summer in Britain. Tick the ones that are correct. Remember: the Earth is rotating on its own axis.

The South Pole is in constant darkness.	
The sunlight reaching Britain is spread over a large area.	
The North Pole is in constant daylight.	
The sunlight reaching Britain is spread over a small area.	
The South Pole is in constant daylight.	
The North Pole is in constant darkness.	

■ Describe what happens to the seasons as the Earth orbits the Sun. Explain why the changes happen, and say how long the changes take.

_____

_____

_____

_____

_____

I can understand what happens to the seasons as Earth orbits the Sun.

How did you do?

Name: _____   Date: _____

Star patterns

■ Use secondary sources and the internet to label these star constellations.

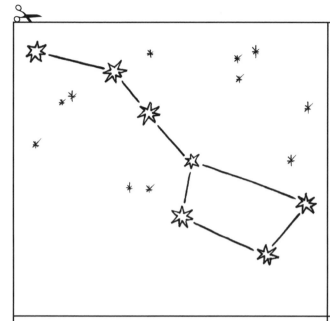
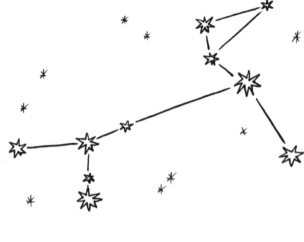
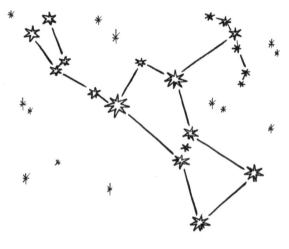
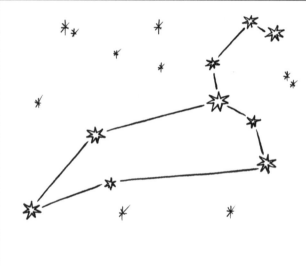
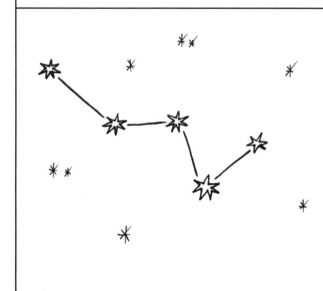
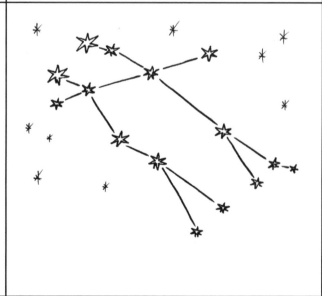

PHOTOCOPIABLE

■SCHOLASTIC
www.scholastic.co.uk

Earth and space

- Well done! You have completed the Earth and space topic!
- Fill in each star below with something you think you have done well or enjoyed during this topic.

- What two things could you have done better and do you need to look at again before you do the assessments for this topic?

I can assess the progress I am making on my knowledge of Earth and space.

How did you do?

All living things: plant life cycles

Expected prior learning
- Know the different parts of flowering plants.
- Know the requirements of plants for life and growth.
- Have some knowledge of seed formation and seed dispersal.
- Know plants are suited to and adapt to their environment in different ways.
- Understand living things have changed over time and that fossils provide information about living things that inhabited the Earth millions of years ago.

Overview of progression
- Describe the life cycles common to a variety of plants.
- Give reasons for classifying plants based on specific characteristics.
- Use classification keys for plants.
- Identify and name a variety of flowering plants: single and composite flowers, monocots and dicots.
- Understand the differences between insect- and wind-pollinated plants.
- Identify different plant life cycles: annuals, biennials, herbaceous and woody perennials.
- Identify the features of plants and how they have adapted in a range of environments: rainforest, in the sea and in the desert.
- Identify some prehistoric plants.
- Appreciate the work of early botanists in the classification of plants.

Creative context
- This chapter provides the opportunity to interest and enthuse children about plant life. There are many opportunities to draw diagrams, sketch flowers or take digital photographs which could link with their art work.
- Through understanding the importance of plants in the wider world for food, our own survival and the environment children have the opportunity to appreciate global issues such as concern over the demise of the rainforests.
- There are also several opportunities to assess children's writing skills during the course of the chapter.

Background knowledge
Plants can be classified into flowering plants and non-flowering plants (conifers, ferns, mosses). This simple classification is based on how plants have evolved and adapted for survival over time. Flowering plants may also be identified by their pollination process, seed dispersal process, adaptation to different climates and their leaf and root structure.

Speaking scientifically
- Classification and Latin terms are explained in the course of the relevant lessons. Children should be encouraged to use the correct terms as much as possible to enhance their knowledge.

Preparation
You will need to provide: examples of as many real plants as you can or photographs of different plants, access to an outdoor location where children can see and identify different plants, access to ICT for display to undertake their own research to enhance their learning and understanding, digital cameras will be useful for outside work in plant identification, some small pots or plastic cups, compost and seeds so that children can *grow their own*.

On the CD-ROM you will find: photocopiable pages 'Seed germination', 'Map of the World', 'Theophrastus', 'John Ray', 'How plants make their own food', 'Plant adaptation', 'Plant reproduction'; media resources 'Seaweed', 'Horsetail fern'

Chapter at a glance

Week	Lesson	Curriculum objectives	Lesson objectives	Main activity	Working scientifically
1	1	• (Y3) To identify and describe the functions of the different parts of flowering plants: roots, stem, leaves and flowers. • (Y4) To explore and use classification keys to help group, identify and name a variety of living things in their local and wider environment. • To describe the life process of reproduction in some plants and animals.	• To revise the parts of flowering plants. • To review classification keys. • To revise how plants can be classified according to their characteristics. • To begin to consider life cycles.	Recapping on how plants are living organisms. Devising a key to separate moss, fern, conifer and flowering plants.	• Recording data and results of increasing complexity using scientific diagrams and labels, classification keys, tables, scatter graphs, bar and line graphs. • Using relevant scientific language and illustrations to discuss, communicate and justify their scientific ideas.
	2	• To describe the life process of reproduction in some plants and animals.	• To know the processes that take place in germination.	Investigating if seeds need water, warmth and light. Predicting sequence of future events and checking as germination proceeds.	• Planning different types of scientific enquiries to answer questions, including recognising and controlling variables where necessary. • Reporting and presenting findings from enquiries.
	3	• To describe the life process of reproduction in some plants and animals.	• To know the structure of single and composite flowers.	Comparing a diagram with a real single flower. Distinguishing single flowers from composite flowers.	• Recording data and results of increasing complexity using scientific diagrams and labels, classification keys, tables, scatter graphs, bar and line graphs.
2	1	• To describe the life process of reproduction in some plants and animals.	• To know the pollen-producing and pollen-receiving parts of the flower. • To know the pollinating insects.	Making a pollen collector, examining pollen and identifying pollinating insects.	• Reporting and presenting findings from enquiries, including conclusions, causal relationships and explanations of and degree of trust in results, in oral and written forms such as displays and other presentations.
	2	• To describe the life process of reproduction in some plants and animals.	• To know wind-pollinated plants and the structure of their flowers. • To know the importance of wind pollination to cereal crops.	Examining the structure of wind-pollinated flowers and relating them to their function.	• Reporting and presenting findings from enquiries, including conclusions, causal relationships and explanations of and degree of trust in results, in oral and written forms such as displays and other presentations.
	3	• To describe the life process of reproduction in some plants and animals.	• To consider the diversity of seed dispersal. • To understand the ways in which seeds are dispersed.	Examining and describing the dispersal methods of a wide range of seeds.	• Reporting and presenting findings from enquiries.
3	1	• *To observe and compare the life cycle of plants in their local environment.*	• To learn to distinguish between ephemerals, annuals, biennials, herbaceous perennials and woody perennials.	Classifying plants according to whether they are annuals, biennials, herbaceous or woody perennials.	
	2	• To describe the life process of reproduction in some plants and animals.	• To learn the plants in a habitat using botanical vocabulary.	Visiting a habitat, making observations and notes on the plants and producing a description of them.	• Reporting and presenting findings from enquiries.
	3	• *To observe and compare the life cycle of plants in their local environment.*	• To understand how plants have adapted to life in a rainforest.	Examining a range of rainforest plants and relating their structures to the functions they carry out in helping the plant survive.	• Recording data and results of increasing complexity using scientific diagrams and labels, classification keys, tables, scatter graphs, bar and line graphs.

Chapter at a glance

Week	Lesson	Curriculum objectives	Lesson objectives	Main activity	Working scientifically
4	1	• To observe and compare the life cycle of plants in their local environment.	• To learn how seaweeds are adapted for shore life.	Investigating the habitat of seaweed and how it is adapted for survival in its habitat.	• Reporting and presenting findings from enquiries, including conclusions, causal relationships and explanations of and degree of trust in results, in oral and written forms such as displays and other presentations.
	2	• To observe and compare the life cycle of plants in their local environment.	• To learn about how plant life cycles are adapted for desert conditions.	Answering questions using information about desert plant life cycles. Investigating how water travels through the stem of a plant.	• Planning different types of scientific enquiries to answer questions, including recognising and controlling variables where necessary. • Reporting and presenting findings from enquiries, including conclusions, causal relationships and explanations of and degree of trust in results, in oral and written forms such as displays and other presentations.
	3	• To describe the life process of reproduction in some plants and animals.	• To learn about prehistoric plants. • To know a living fossil.	Investigating plant fossil formation. Modelling the creation of a fossil.	• Using simple models to describe scientific ideas.
5	1	• To find out about the work of naturalists.	• To learn about Theophrastus and his work on plants.	Finding out about the life and work of Theophrastus and its relevance today.	• Identifying scientific evidence that has been used to support or refute ideas or arguments.
	2	• To find out about the work of naturalists.	• To learn about John Ray and his work on plants.	Finding out about the life and work of John Ray. Identifying monocotyledons and dicotyledons by their leaf structure.	• Identifying scientific evidence that has been used to support or refute ideas or arguments.
	3	• To find out about the work of naturalists.	• To learn about Joseph Banks and his work on plants. • To learn about the work done by Kew researchers.	Finding out about the Joseph Banks and the work of Kew Gardens. Researching the plants we use.	• Reporting and presenting findings from enquiries, including conclusions, causal relationships and explanations of and degree of trust in results, in oral and written forms such as displays and other presentations.
6	1	• To describe the life process of reproduction in some plants and animals.	• To understand how plants and trees make their own food.	Labelling the process of photosynthesis and writing about this process using their own words.	• Using relevant scientific language and illustrations to discuss, communicate and justify their scientific ideas.
	2	• To describe the life process of reproduction in some plants and animals.	• To learn how bulbs and tubers grow.	Investigating bulbs and other geophytes and finding out how they are different. Growing a geophyte.	• Using relevant scientific language and illustrations to discuss, communicate and justify their scientific ideas.
	3	• To observe life cycle changes in plants in the vegetable garden or flower border.	• To understand the requirements of plants when setting up a garden, flower bed or vegetable plot.	Using gathered evidence about plant life as the basis for a gardening project. Planning the project and carrying it out.	• Planning different types of scientific enquiries to answer questions, including recognising and controlling variables where necessary.
Assess and review					

Objectives
- To revise the parts of flowering plants.
- To review classification keys.
- To revise how plants can be classified according to their characteristics.
- To begin to consider life cycles.

Resources
Photocopiable page 135 'Labelled flower'; some fir branches or cones; plants with dead flowers which have seeds; some ferns and some moss

Speaking scientifically
root, leaf, stem, flower, fruit, seeds, key, flowering plants, conifers, ferns, mosses, classification, habitat, botanist

Lesson 1: What do we know about plants?

Previous knowledge
This lesson draws together the children's previous knowledge on plants and will feature the parts of a flowering plant and their functions and the elementary classification of plants.

Introduction
Remind the children that they learned a lot about plants in Years 3 and 4. Ask: *What is a plant?* Write some of the children's answers on the board even though they may be examples of plants rather than saying what a plant is. If the response *organism* or *living thing* is given then circle these and ask children if the other examples they have given are living or dead. Establish that a plant is a living organism and remind them that a plant must follow all the seven life processes:

- movement: even though it is anchored to the ground a plant will move towards the sun to get as much light as it can
- reproduction: it produces seeds which turn into new plants
- sensitivity: it can detect change, for example heat and cold
- growth: it grows bigger
- respiration: it breathes
- excretion: it gives out oxygen
- nutrition: it takes in food, by making its own food using sunlight.

Tell children that the three processes for plants that they need to know about are nutrition, growth and reproduction.

Independent work
1. Explain that each part of a flowering plant has a special role to play and ask each child to draw a full page picture of a flowering plant and ask them to label the flowers, leaves, stem and roots.

2. Show the diagram on photocopiable page 135 'Labelled flower' and compare it with the children's drawings.

Whole-class/paired work
3. In pairs, ask the children to write down what they know about each part of the plant that has been labelled. Ask: *How do you think each part helps in the life processes of reproduction, nutrition and growth?*

4. Under the four headings *flowers*, *leaves*, *stem* and *roots* get feedback from the class and note this down. Reinforce the children's understanding by asking them to write down the function of each part of the plant next to the labels on their diagrams.

Whole-class work
5. Remind the children how scientists or botanists divide or classify plants into different groups. Ask the children to think of some categories in which plants could be grouped. There are many possibilities, for example: trees, shrubs, grasses, small flowering plants; or desert plants, tropical plants, temperate plants; or evergreen plants, deciduous plants.

6. Write the children's suggestions for categories on the board and then ask them to think of names of some plants. Write the plants+ names next to the appropriate category listed on the board.

7. Explain that, regardless of size or where plants grow, scientists or botanists who study plants have classified them according to how they have evolved over time on the planet. This involves looking at their vascular or circulation system which is how they send nutrients from the ground to the rest of the plant and the way they reproduce. The four main groups of plants used for classification are:

Checkpoint
● Do children understand the function of roots, stems, flowers and leaves?
● Do they understand that plants flourish in different conditions?
● Do they understand that plants vary in type?
● Do they understand how plants may be classified?

● Mosses: These are very small plants about 1in or 2cm high with no stem. They have no vascular system, which is a series of tubes within the stem, leaves or petals that can transport or circulate water and nutrients through the plant, so mosses remain small. They also require water to enable their reproductive cells to combine.
● Ferns: These were the first plants to develop a vascular or circulatory system that lets them grow larger. They have roots, leaves, stems, and trunks. They also need water to reproduce without producing seeds but because they have a vascular system they can grow very large.
● Conifers: Since conifers grow so tall it is not so surprising that they have a vascular or circulation system. They have also, however, developed the ability to create seeds so they can reproduce and are evergreen. They rely on the wind to spread their seeds and do not have flowers, which is the next stage in the story of plant evolution.

8. Flowering plants have a vascular system to help them grow bigger. They produce seeds but they also have flowers which are able to attract insects to help pollinate and spread their seeds around. Their seeds are also contained in a fruit, often eaten by animals and birds, which also helps to spread their seeds across much wider areas.

Paired work

9. Remind children about the keys they produced to identify animals then ask them, using the information above, to use a key to identify a flowering plant, a conifer, a fern and a moss. You could then ask them to test their key using some of the plants that they wrote down earlier. Some hints which might help are:

- Does it flower?
- Does it have seeds?
- Does it have a circulation or vascular system?

Introducing the new area of study

Challenge the children to define *life cycle* and look for an answer about the stages in the development of a living organism. Tell them that they are going to be finding out about the life cycle of plants.

> **Differentiation**
> ● Support children by helping them to set out the questions they need to ask or they can use the key given in the review to decide on their yes/no responses.
> ● Challenge children to produce a key without any extra hints, but it may help to suggest some questions; please see the review.

Science in the wider world

Plants are hugely important in our world. They absorb carbon dioxide and other gases from the air and give out oxygen that we need to breathe. We also eat a huge range of produce from plants: cereals, fruits, vegetables.

Review

Ask a child to draw out their key for you. One suggestion is as follows:

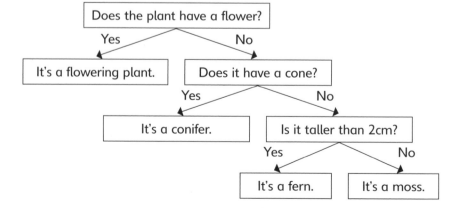

Objectives
● To know the processes that take place in germination.

Resources
Photocopiable page 'Seed germination' from the CD-ROM; a variety of large seeds such as runner beans, dwarf beans or nasturtiums; a range of pairs of small flowerpots; some identical clear plastic containers; sheets of absorbent paper; a variety of peat-free composts; small trowels or old spoons; containers to measure small amounts of water; labels; elastic bands

Speaking scientifically
germination, seedling, fair test, variable, conditions, constant

Lesson 2: Germination

Introduction
The main purpose of this lesson is to devise and conduct a scientific experiment rather than necessarily grow a plant successfully. Explain to children that the word *germinate* means *to sprout*. Ask what conditions they think seeds need in order to germinate and list these (water, light and warmth). If warmth is omitted from the list ask: *Why do people use greenhouses to grow seeds?* You will also need to explain that soil is not necessarily needed for seeds to germinate. Show the photocopiable page 'Seed germination' from the CD-ROM. If children query the need for light, explain that although seeds may shoot and initially develop seed leaves, if they remain in the dark they will not flourish into adult plants without light which gives them food.

Whole-class work
1. Tell the children that they are going to choose from a range of materials so that they can test their skills in experimental design. Allow them to choose their seeds and then decide whether to use pots and soil or absorbent paper.

2. Emphasise that they will be testing the right conditions for the seeds to germinate and they will be testing one factor: warmth, moisture or light. Consequently, when children choose their equipment, the pair of pots must be the *same*, the seed type and number of seeds must be the *same* and their planting material, soil or absorbent paper, must be the *same* for both pots.

Paired/group work
3. Once children have chosen their pots, seeds and planting material show them how they should plant them and, as appropriate, how much water to give each pot each day.

4. Ask them to discuss which variable they are going to test so that they are conducting a fair test. What do they think will happen?

5. Make sure that they label each pot with seed type and planting material and how they will tend each pot, listing the testing factors.

6. Ask them to write down a title for their experiment, the materials used, how they have organised it and most especially the factor they are testing for: warmth, moisture or light.

7. Once the seed with access to all three variables has become a thriving plant, ask the children to complete their report on the experiment and explain what has happened and why, using diagrams if they wish.

> ### Differentiation
> ● Support children by helping them to recognise that one pot should have warmth, moisture and light with one of these variables omitted when tendering the second pot.
> ● Challenge children to set up the experiment independently without help.

Science in the wider world
Gardeners and farmers help seeds to germinate through using a greenhouse or they erect polytunnels in the fields. Both these structures are designed to keep seeds warm.

Review
Discuss the outcomes from all the experiments with the whole class. Ask: *Were the outcomes as you expected?*

Resources
Photocopiable page 136 'Parts of a flower'; large single flowers such as tiger lilies or daffodils (one for each child); example of a composite flower such as a daisy or dandelion; plastic knives; cutting boards, magnifying glasses; paper for mounting; sticky tape; visualiser or electron microscope (optional)

Speaking scientifically
stamen, anther, filament, stigma, ovary, sepal, petal, pollen, single flower, composite flower

Lesson 3: Flower structure

Introduction

Show children photocopiable page 136 'Parts of a flower'. Describe the function of each part:

● stem: supports the flower
● sepal: protects the flower bud
● petal: the colourful part that that attracts the pollinators, usually insects
● stamen: is the male part of the flower and includes the anther and the filament
● anther: produces pollen cells – each one contains a male sex cell
● filament: supports the anther
● pistil: is the female part of the plant and includes the stigma, style and ovary
● stigma: the part of the plant that captures pollen
● style: the pollen travels down the style towards the ovary
● ovary: stores the female sex cells called ovules which are fertilised by pollen to produce a seed or fruit.

Explain to the children that the diagram shows a single flower, but there are also flowers that are composite flowers – such as daisies. Show them the daisy and point out how the petals form rays around a disc in the centre.

Whole-class work

1. Tell the children that you are going to show them how to dissect a real single flower so that they can see the individual parts. If you have access to a digital microscope or a visualiser use this to display the individual parts.

2. Cut the lily or daffodil flower down the middle. Remove the following parts and re-explain their function: stem, sepals, petals.

3. Next, remove a stamen and show the anther and the filament. Show how the anther has pollen and collect a sample on a piece of sticky tape.

4. Finally, show the pistil with the stigma, style and ovary and reveal where the ovules or eggs are hidden which can usually be seen with a magnifying glass.

5. Using the stamen explain that the male sex cell travels from the pollen grain down the stigma in a pollen tube to the ovary to fertilise an ovule to produce a seed.

Independent work

6. Ask children to dissect their own flowers. They should stick each part, including a sample of pollen, on a piece of paper and label it using the words from the diagram shown earlier.

7. Distribute magnifying glasses so that they can observe the different parts of a flower more closely.

> **Differentiation**
> ● Support children by suggesting they label only the major features.
> ● Challenge children to write down and describe the different parts of the flower they have just dissected.

Science in the wider world

Flowers not only look attractive and add colour to the landscape, but they also produce the many fruits we eat and, through the seeds they produce, the cereals we eat which are essential for our survival.

Review

Display the children's work and ask some children to show you the different parts of the flower.

Objectives
- To know the pollen-producing and pollen-receiving parts of the flower.
- To know the pollinating insects.

Resources
Photocopiable page 136 'Parts of a flower'; an area of flowers such as a garden or park; clipboards; photocopiable page 137 'Pollinator observation sheet'

Speaking scientifically
pollen, pollination, anther, stigma, stamen, style, ovary, fertilisation, species

Lesson 1: Insect pollination

Introduction
Show the children photocopiable page 136 'Parts of a flower' and explain to them that pollination means that pollen is taken from the male part of a flower, the anther, and enters the female part of the flower, the stigma so that fertilisation of the seed takes place. This process enables the female part of the flower to produce seeds to create new plants. Ask how flowers are pollinated (by the wind or insects and occasionally by birds or animals). Explain that this lesson is about insect pollination.

Whole-class work
1. Choose a warm sunny day and tell children that they are going to investigate pollination for themselves and write a report.

2. Visit the flowered area and give out photocopiable page 137 'Pollinator observation sheet' and clipboards.

3. Demonstrate how to lift a little pollen from the flower using the sticky tape and how to fix this onto their sheets in the place given.

Individual/paired work
4. Ask them to choose a flower to observe and then to draw it. Warn them not to get too close to bees or wasps.

5. Next they should to spend ten minutes observing their flowers to see which insects visit them and note this on the tally chart on the sheet.

6. Explain that they must keep their sheets carefully as they will be using the diagrams, pollen and data collected in their reports once they are back in the classroom.

7. When back in the classroom ask the children to write a report of their investigation, giving details of their chosen plant, the insects they observed visiting its flowers and any other observations.

> ### Differentiation
> - Support children by helping them to draw their flowers or by using a digital camera.
> - Challenge children to complete the task with minimal help.

Science in the wider world
Insect pollination is important not only in the production of honey from bees, but also in the fertilisation of many fruit trees.

Review
Draw the data from all the class together and see if there are any conclusions you can investigate such as: *Which insects were the most common pollinators? Was there a most popular colour of flower? Which were the most popular plants?*

Objectives
● To know wind-pollinated plants and the structure of their flowers.
● To know the importance of wind pollination to cereal crops.

Resources
Some examples of different grasses which are in flower; old cereal boxes or the ingredients labels from cereal boxes; bread wrappers (especially from multigrain bread); cereal bar wrappers; biscuit wrappers

Speaking scientifically
pollination, grass, cereal, wheat, maize, barley, oats, rice, rye, fertilisation, stamen, stigma

Lesson 2: Wind pollination

Introduction

Ask the children what they ate for breakfast and write down some of their answers on the board. Assuming that the likely answers are toast or various kinds of breakfast cereal, tell them that what they ate was pollinated by the wind. Bread is made of wheat and breakfast cereals are usually made from cereals such as wheat, rice, oats, maize or barley. Other kinds of common plants which are usually pollinated by the wind are grasses and most trees. Tell children that in the next part of the lesson they will find out how wind pollination works and then investigate in more detail what they really ate for breakfast.

Whole-class work

1. Explain that as insects play no part in wind pollination, the flowers of these plants do not need to develop brightly coloured petals, a scent or nectar to attract them. However, wind-pollinated plants do have flowers, but the children might not recognise them as flowers!

2. Show the children the grasses and point out the feathery flowers. Explain that the process of fertilisation is the same for wind-pollinated plants as it is for insect-pollinated ones (the pollen must pass from the stamen to the stigma). For this to happen both these parts need to be on the outside of the plant. The plant has no petals and the stigma is feathery so that pollen can easily reach and interact with it.

3. Talk about how, as the wind blows, pollen is blown through the structure of the stigma which creates the opportunity for fertilisation.

Paired work

4. Ask children to draw a table with cereals: wheat, maize, barley, rice, oats, rye listed along the top and the names of the food products they are going to investigate down the side.

5. Explain that if, for example, wheat flour, or maize flour is on the list of ingredients then this should be included as wheat or maize.

6. Tell them that they should put a tick by the appropriate food product for each cereal that is on the list of ingredients.

7. Ask them to examine the information in their tables and write down what they found in a report.

> **Differentiation**
> ● Support children by helping them to write down what they found using prompt questions such as: *Which cereal is most used in food products?*, *Which is used least?*, *Which food product contains the most cereals?*
> ● Challenge children to create separate tables for breakfast cereals, cereal bars and bread and biscuits.

Science in the wider world

Grasses and wind-pollinated plants have fine, light pollen so that it is easily blown by the wind. For this reason a common effect of grass pollen is hay fever, though other plants and trees may also cause hay fever.

Review

Discuss the findings from the children's reports with the whole class and see if they can draw any conclusions from the sample of food products that they eat for breakfast.

Lesson 3: Seed dispersal

Introduction

Ask children if they can remember from earlier work any of the ways seeds are dispersed and note their responses. Starting with the ways that children have mentioned explain briefly how dispersion occurs. The most common methods of dispersion are by:

● animals: some seeds have hooks or sticky surfaces which attach to an animal as they brush past them which are then carried some distance before they are later deposited to the ground. Others such as acorns or hazelnuts may be buried as a food store but remain unused so may later germinate. Animals and particularly birds eat the fruit of plants which contain seeds, for example, berries from trees, strawberries or raspberries which they later excrete far from the parent plant where the seeds start to grow.
● water: willow and silver birch trees often grow by a stream. They have small light seeds which are easily carried by wind or water. Similarly foxgloves and harebells have light seeds that float. Coconuts on the other hand are heavy but will float in the sea and may be transported a long way before they settle in a new spot.
● explosion: some plants have seed pods which explode so that the seeds are carried some distance away from the parent plant. Examples of these are: lupines and gorse.
● wind: some seeds are blown from the plant.

Whole-class work

1. Show the children the samples of seeds that you have brought in and identify how they are dispersed. Point out the features they have that make dispersal successful. For example, the wings of a sycamore seed which help it to glide in the wind.

2. Ask children to bring in a variety of fruits and seeds from plants and trees with as great a variety as possible and remind them that they should always wash their hands after handling these.

Paired work

3. Ask children to name some of the seeds they recognise and sort them into how they think they are dispersed.

4. Ask them to use the internet to find out further information in order to write a report on some of the seeds they have collected, drawing diagrams where necessary and stating the special features the seeds have to help dispersal.

Differentiation
● Support children in recognising their seeds and writing up their report by asking questions such as: *Does the seed have wings?*, *Do you think an animal might eat this?*
● Challenge children to write down all the seeds they can think of including those in fruits and say how they think they are dispersed using reference books or the internet if necessary.

Science in the wider world

Although nature has its own way of dispersing seeds, in the commercial world farmers and gardeners do not rely on nature to ensure that they get a good crop or a beautiful garden. Instead they collect seeds themselves and sow them carefully to ensure that they have adequate space to grow and thrive.

Review

Ask the pairs to report their findings back to the class, then ask them to complete photocopiable page 138 'Seeds'.

Objectives
● To learn to distinguish between ephemerals, annuals, biennials, herbaceous perennials and woody perennials.

Resources
Plant or seed catalogues; a list of common trees and plants (see right); photocopiable page 139 'Plant life cycle'

Speaking scientifically
ephemerals, annuals, biennials, herbaceous perennials, woody perennials

Lesson 1: Plant life cycles

Introduction
Ask children what they know about the life cycle of a flowering plant reminding them of the different stages: germination, growth, pollination, fertilisation, seed production and seed dispersal. Emphasise that if any of these stages are omitted then the cycle cannot be completed to produce new growth. Give the class photocopiable page 139 'Plant life cycle' to complete. Tell them that as well as putting them in order by numbering each stage they should write down the name of the stage reached on each of the pictures if they can. When they have completed the task discuss the life cycle with them to ensure that they understand the sequence of events.

Group/paired work
1. Explain that although plants have the same life cycle the length of the life cycles of different plants varies hugely. Plants are usually classified on the basis of how long the plant lives before it dies: ephemerals (live for less than a growing season), annuals (live for one growing season), biennials (live for two growing seasons), and perennials (live for many growing seasons). There are two types of perennial: herbaceous perennials have stems that die at the end of the growing season, leaving a root or bulb to grow again next season; woody perennials have woody stems that remain alive during the non-growing season and grow shoots the next year.

2. Give out the plant and seed catalogues or, if unavailable, write a list of plants on the board, for example, tulip, oak tree, privet hedge, rose, bluebell, grass, sunflower, geranium, daisy, strawberry, carrot, raspberry, apple, potato, pear, chrysanthemum, lobelia, plum, horse chestnut tree, dandelion. Ask the children to write down how many of the plants they recognise.

3. Next ask them to classify them according to whether they are annuals, biennials, herbaceous perennials or woody perennials thinking about what the plant looks like and where they see it growing.

4. Ask them to record this data in a table and by cutting out the pictures from the catalogues to create a display of their data.

Differentiation
● Support children according to their knowledge of garden plants. Some children may find this task easier than others and so try to mix groups so that children can help each other. Ask them to start with the plants they know best rather than getting stuck on the ones they have little knowledge of.
● Challenge children by asking them to investigate some of the common vegetables we eat such as potatoes, carrots, cabbages and broccoli and classify the plants relating to these.

Science in the wider world
In recent years, scientists have done a great deal of work on creating perennial crops such as wheat and rice to save the process of planting seeds each year. This means that food can be more easily mass produced.

Review
Ask children, in their groups, to present their displays and explain them to the rest of the class.

Objectives

- To learn the plants in a habitat using botanical vocabulary.

Resources

A local habitat containing flowers and plants such as garden or park; clipboards (one between two); a reference book on wild flowers, plants and trees; digital cameras (if available); rulers; photocopiable page 140 'Habitats'; internet access

Speaking scientifically

habitat, environment, species, moss, fern, conifer, flowering plant

Lesson 2: Plants in their habitat

Introduction

Explain that some of the plants the children may see growing in a garden or park in the UK today may have originally come from another part of the world, with a different climate and different soil. Consequently, the plants growing in gardens and parks do not necessarily represent the plants that grow or survive easily in our local habitat. Plants in these areas may have been specially planted, been germinated in a greenhouse, be planted in special soil or watered frequently. Remind the class that growth and survival includes the ability of the plant to reproduce and that the whole growth cycle is: germination, growth, pollination, fertilisation, seed production and seed dispersal.

Whole-class work

1. Tell children that they are going to visit a local habitat to observe what grows there. Ask them to think of different plant habitats that may exist within an area of natural growth, given that plant growth depends on water, temperature, light and the soil they are grown in.

2. Write their suggestions on the board (these may include: sunny, shady, wet, dry, thick vegetation, woodland, hedgerows, the seashore, close to a wall).

Paired work

3. At the habitat, give each pair a clipboard and photocopiable page 140 'Habitats', to note down the species of plant that they observe and where it is growing. Emphasise that children should not pick any plants or flowers.

4. Take a reference book with you on plants so that you can help with identification. Point out that all plants have two names, a common name and a Latin name. Encourage children to find out the Latin names of the plants they are familiar with and the common and Latin names for plants that they don't know.

5. While they are observing ask them to:

- differentiate between shady or sunny areas as the shady areas will naturally be both cooler and wetter than the drier ones
- try to name the plants or trees they find, draw a diagram or take a photo
- differentiate between mosses, ferns, conifers and flowering plants;
- note the size of the leaves each time and draw these;
- estimate, or if possible measure, the height of the plants they observe
- note the growth cycle of the plants: germinating, flowering or have seed pods.

6. When back in the classroom, ask the children to write a report on which plants they observed in different habitats using their drawings or digital images.

> ### Differentiation
>
> - Support children in identifying particular species, encouraging them to use the internet, CD-ROMs or reference books for identification. Less confident learners may also need help in writing their report.
> - Challenge children to draw up a table of all the plants they have found to show where they grow and whether they are flowering or non-flowering plants. Ask them if they can give a hypothesis for the conditions under which each type of plant grows.

Science in the wider world

In all areas of the world it is important to preserve the local environment and the plant species as they live in their natural environment.

Review

Ask several of the children to present their findings. Ask other children to tell you if they observed other plant species which have not been mentioned, then make a table collectively of all the species found. Display the work in the classroom. Emphasise the need to look after local habitats so that species of plants are preserved in their natural surroundings.

● To understand how plants have adapted to life in a rainforest.

Resources
Photocopiable page 'Map of the World' from the CD-ROM; any house plants available which are tropical in origin such as orchids; bromeliads and stems from a clematis or passion flower

Speaking scientifically
epiphytes, bromeliad, orchid, liana, carnivorous, canopy, clematis, passion flower

Lesson 3: Rainforest plants

Introduction
Use the photocopiable page 'Map of the world' from the CD-ROM and point out where tropical rainforests are found along the line of the equator. Explain that tropical rainforests cover only a small part of the earth's surface – about 6%, yet they are home to over half the species of plants and animals in the world. Talk about the characteristics of the rainforests and how the animals and plants that exist there must learn to adapt to this climate.

Whole-class work
1. Explain to the children that the plant life in a rainforest exists in several layers (the canopy, the understory, and the forest floor) and that each layer has its own specific features.

2. Show the children the plants you have brought in and explain that these all originally come from the rainforest and are therefore uniquely adapted to the conditions found in this habitat.

3. Talk about where they are found and the specific ways that each plant has adapted. (For example, orchids have air roots which help them to absorb water and nutrients in the rainforest, liana is a climbing vine that grows on rainforest trees so its leaves get more sunlight, the Pitcher plant is carnivorous.)

Paired/individual work
4. Ask the children to carry out their own research on rainforest plants through the following tasks, either in school or for homework:
● Which plants do we eat that come from the rainforest?
● What is the name of the largest plant in the world and where does it live?
● What does a bromeliad look like? Draw a diagram of this species and explain the way they capture water.
● Draw a diagram of a rainforest showing all the different layers of plant life.

> **Differentiation**
> ● Support children by suggesting some appropriate internet sites that would help them to find the information they need.
> ● Challenge children by asking them to investigate the rainforest plants that are important for herbal and medical cures and to explain their findings to the rest of the class.

Science in the wider world
Between a half and two thirds of the world's plant species are found in the tropical rainforests and new species are still being discovered. Recently, a great interest in rainforest plants has developed as a source of new medicines and to provide cures for illnesses. Rainforest plants also provide shelter and food for rare animals and insects. Perhaps more importantly, they create much of the world's oxygen supply which humans need for survival. It is largely for this reason that there is such concern about the destruction of the rainforest areas.

Review
Ask the children, either individually or in groups, to give a presentation to the whole class about their research. There is a great deal still to learn about rainforest plants so encourage them to discover more and do further research in their own time.

Objectives
● To learn how seaweeds are adapted for the sea life.

Resources
Seaweed (a local aquarium or fish shop usually has some stock); media resource 'Seaweed' on the CD-ROM; a trip to the beach (optional); internet access

Speaking scientifically
seaweed, algae, seagrass, holdfast, sargassum, vascular structure, kelp, multi-cellular, primary producer

Lesson 1: Plant life in the sea

Introduction
Tell the children that in this lesson they are going to look at how seaweed adapts itself to living in the sea. Look at the media resource 'Seaweed' on the CD-ROM and explain that there are over 10,000 varieties of seaweed in the world. Show children the air bags on the seaweed, its flat leaves and its slimy surface. Explain that seaweed is a marine algae rather than a plant because it lacks the vascular structure or circulation system of a plant that allows water or nutrients to be passed through the plant. Seaweed also lacks the leaves, flowers, roots and seeds which would classify it as a flowering plant. However, it often looks like a plant and can grow to very big. For example, giant kelp can grow up to 60m in length and looks a bit like a palm tree, but other seaweeds often look more like moss or a lettuce.

Whole-class work
1. If you live close to the sea take children on a trip to investigate some rock pools and collect some seaweed and examine it in its habitat.

2. Talk about some of the ways that seaweed has adapted to living in the sea by:

● having flat leaves so that they can get as much exposure to the sunlight as possible to produce food

● having air bags which help them to keep near the sea's surface or float so that they can access light

● producing a jelly like substance to help stop them drying out

● attaching themselves to rocks or the seabed with a holdfast to help them remain underwater but these attachments do not act like a root and absorb nutrients.

Group/paired work
3. If you have plentiful access to seaweed, ask the children to design an experiment to find what happens to seaweed when it dries out, is kept in fresh water or is kept in salty water.

4. If you have limited access to seaweed, or only pictures, ask groups to draw a diagram of seaweed, label the parts and say how the seaweed adapts to living underwater.

5. Ask children to use the internet to find images of different seaweeds.

> **Differentiation**
> ● Support children by asking them to label the parts on the picture of seaweed showing how seaweed adapts to its environment to ensure that they grasp the main points.
> ● Challenge children by asking them to find out, using the internet if necessary, the importance of seaweed and other underwater plants to the survival of all life in the sea.

Science in the wider world
Seaweed is rich in vitamins and minerals and is therefore used for many different things: as a food and as an ingredient in medicines and beauty products. Some species of seaweed are grown commercially for use in fertilisers and people who live by the sea sometimes visit the shore to collect seaweed for the garden. However, not all seaweeds have positive uses. Sargassum can choke native varieties of seaweed which can affect the ecology and species of fish able to survive in the area.

Review
Draw together children's work and ask different groups to discuss what they have found out about seaweed. Display their work on a display board.

Resources
cacti; celery sticks; water; different food colourings; plastic cups; plastic knives

Speaking scientifically
succulent, cactus, cacti, transpire

Lesson 2: Desert plants

Introduction

Talk about the desert habitat and relate this to the conditions plants need for their life cycle (very hot, little and infrequent rainfall, sandy and rocky soil that holds little water, strong drying winds). Explain that there are few plants that grow in the desert but the ones that do have adapted to cope with these extreme conditions of heat and drought. Tell children that cacti are the best known species of desert plant although there are others which have a different life cycle from a cactus.

Whole-class work

1. Show the children your cacti and explain that they are succulents and point out the relevant features if appropriate to your plants. Cacti have:
● thick leathery leaves that enable them to store water
● wide stems, which may be the whole plant and which are designed to store water
● few leaves to reduce water loss
● spines which help prevent animals and birds from drinking the moisture from their fleshy trunk or leaves
● leaves with hair to shade the plant, to reduce water loss
● long roots that spread out wide or go deep into the ground to absorb as much water as possible when it does rain
● a waxy coating on their stems and leaves to help reduce water loss;
● slow growth as this requires less energy and the plant to make less food, reducing the amount of water it needs.

Group work

2. Explain that the children are going to use celery stalks to model how the stalks of a cactus draw in water through their stems.

3. Give each group cups, two celery sticks, some water and a small amount of food colouring. Ask them how they might design an experiment to see how water reaches the leaves on the celery stalk and to test if the stalk survives without access to water.

4. Check how children intend to do their investigation and if necessary give them the following prompts:
● Pour a small amount of water into one cup, add 15 drops of colouring and stir the mixture. Put one celery stalk into this cup.
● Put the second stalk into a cup with no water.
● Leave for one or two days and notice the condition of each stalk.
● Cut each piece of celery in half and describe what has happened.

5. Ask the children to write a report on the investigation, using diagrams to show the results and draw conclusions from what has happened.

> **Differentiation**
> ● Support children in writing up their investigation.
> ● Challenge children to design their own experiment without any suggestions on how to use the two cups.

Review

Ask children to draw a picture of a cactus and label and explain some of the features that help it to survive in the desert.

Objectives
- To learn about prehistoric plants.
- To know a *living fossil*.

Resources
Media resource 'Horsetail fern' on the CD-ROM; examples of petrified wood; plant or animal fossils; some fern leaves or if unavailable leaves from trees or plants with an interesting shape; plastic trays or food containers; sand; plaster of Paris; string

Speaking scientifically
fossil, angiosperm, petrified, horsetails, ginkgo, cycad, magnolia, moss, fern, spores

Lesson 3: Prehistoric plants

Introduction
Show the class any samples of fossils that you have so that they are familiar with what fossils look like. The table below shows the relative ages of different species of plants:

Millions of years ago	Plant life on land
543 to 248	The first plants appeared including mosses, horsetails and ferns
206 to 114 (Jurassic)	First seed-bearing plants such as conifers, cypress and ginkgo trees and cycads
144 to 65	Flowering plants existed including magnolias and palms

Explain that while no prehistoric animals have survived in their original form, several species of plant remain virtually unchanged such as horsetail ferns and conifers such as the monkey puzzle tree. Show the children the photograph 'Horsetail fern' on the CD-ROM. Explain that these species reproduce through the dispersal of spores and do not have seeds.

Whole-class work
1. Explain how scientists know about the appearance and evolution of plant life by looking at fossils.

2. Talk about how plant fossils are formed when plant matter (such as stems, leaves, roots, spores, seeds, or fruits) are protected from decomposing. They may become covered with sediment such as clay, mud, sand, or volcanic ash.

3. Tell the class that they are now going to make their own fossilised leaves.

Paired work
4. Tell the children to put plenty of sand in the container and make some flat shallow hollows in it using a small block of wood. Tell them to be careful not to expose the bottom of the container.

5. Next they should lay a leaf in each hollow so that it is flat. Add the plaster of Paris to about 2 litres of water, to make a smooth paste that will still flow. Tell them to pour the plaster of Paris over each hollow and smooth the top.

6. Make a loop with the piece of string and set into one end of the plaster at the top end of the leaf and leave it to dry for at least three hours. The *fossils* can then be picked out using the string and the leaf can be removed from its surface.

Differentiation
- Support children by looking for the veins on their leaves and explain how their model simulates the process of fossilisation.
- Challenge children to find out more about prehistoric plants. Ask them if any are familiar and which ones still survive today.

Science in the wider world
Coal which has provided fuel across the world is a fossil formed from the remains of plants from prehistoric times. It is of course a fossilised fuel so today alternatives are sought to avoid air pollution

Review
Show the whole class how the details of the leaves imprinted on their models are similar to real fossils of plant life and explain that a similar process happens under fossilisation as leaves are embedded between layers of sand and silt. Children may wish to paint their fossils or leave them white. Create a mobile to show the class collection of *fossils*.

Resources
Photocopiable page 'Theophrastus' on the CD-ROM; photocopiable page 141 'Theophrastus: true or false?'

Speaking scientifically
cotton plant, banyan, pepper, cinnamon, frankincense, myrrh, peripatetic

Lesson 1: The first botanist

Introduction
Tell children that in this lesson they will be looking at some of the ideas of Theophrastus, a Greek who lived about 2400 years ago. They will then have to decide, using what we now know, which of his ideas were correct and how they have since changed.

Whole-class work
1. Read through the photocopiable page 'Theophrastus' from the CD-ROM together.

2. Give the children photocopiable page 141 'Theophrastus: true or false?' Look at the statements that Theophrastus thought were true, and tell the children that some of them are still true today and some we now know to be untrue.

3. Discuss the questions before the children complete the sheet and remind them about some of the work they have previously done on plants. A brief discussion of the question statements you may wish to discuss at this stage are given below:

● Plants are now classified according to the way they reproduce rather than their 'woodiness'. The major classification is flowering and non-flowering.
● Plants that exist in the wild have adapted to their habitat and so have overcome any likely diseases unlike cultured plants.
● Trees need sun or at least light but unless conditions are particularly harsh there is no reason to suppose that wind harms trees.
● Since cereals, beans and peas were all grown to be eaten as staple food in Theophrastus' day he classified them in the same plant group. Cereals however are in a different plant group.
● Flowers and leaves do move towards the Sun.
● This is the case unless seeds are very carefully stored under the right conditions of temperature and humidity.
● This statement is true to some extent though Theophrastus had not taken into account that seeds may be dispersed by animals eating the fruit of a plant.

Differentiation
● Support children by reading the questions with them a second time and ask them to answer first those they know are true.
● Challenge children by asking them to explain the underlying reasons for giving each statement true or false.

Science in the wider world
Theophrastus' work was of great importance in classifying plants for the food we eat and he identified many of the cereals, herbs and spices that we still use today.

Review
Despite the pre-discussion of Theophrastus' statements it is worth revisiting these when children have completed their statement sheets as many of these are fundamental to children's understanding of plant life and processes.

Lesson 2: John Ray

Introduction

Tell children that in this lesson they will be looking at some of the ideas of John Ray, another famous botanist, who lived about 400 years ago. He introduced classification systems for organisms and inspired generations afterwards to collect, document, and classify organisms, which began to bring order to the study of species.

Whole-class work

1. Read together the information about John Ray on photocopiable page 'John Ray' from the CD-ROM.

2. Look at the table at the bottom of the sheet and ensure that the children understand the content.

Paired work

3. Give the children photocopiable page 142 'Classifying plants' and ask them to classify the plants listed on the sheet as well as some of the samples of plants you have brought in or they have brought in for themselves. It would be helpful to label these samples A to E and remind them that the terms monocots and dicots refer to only flowering plants.

4. The answers are: rose – dicot; tomato – dicot; daffodil – monocot; Christmas tree – conifer; iris – monocot; carnation – dicot; fern – fern; oak tree – dicot.

Differentiation
- Support children who may not know as much about plants as others.
- Challenge children to find out about the root vegetables we eat or other plants and classify them according to their root structure.

Science in the wider world

John Ray's contribution to the world of science was substantial; he started to classify plants and many other organisms in a systematic way which led to the study of botany and an interest in creating botanical gardens to display the range of different species that we know today.

Review

Check through the results of the children's classifications.

Objectives
- To learn about the John Ray and his work on plants.

Resources
Photocopiable page 'John Ray' from the CD-ROM; photocopiable page 142 'Classifying plants'; sprigs of a tomato plant, privet bushes; grasses, daisies, dandelions or plant cuttings of your choice or use those brought in by the class

Speaking scientifically
organism, monocotyledon (monocots), variegated, veins, tap root, secondary roots, herbaceous, seed leaf, pore, classification

Objectives
● To learn about Joseph Banks and his work on plants.
● To learn about the work done by Kew researchers.

Speaking scientifically
conserve, species, naturalist

Lesson 3: Joseph Banks

Introduction

Explain that Joseph Banks was born in 1743 and had a passion for botany from a young age. He travelled all over the world, collecting a huge number of plants and animal specimens before settling in London where he built a huge library and herbarium. He was elected President of the Royal Society in 1771 and became unofficial director of Kew Gardens which became one of the best botanical gardens in the world under his leadership. His collection of plants and insects is now held at the museum at Kew but perhaps the greatest things he did was to exchange so many species of plants between the UK and the rest of the world.

Whole-class work

1. Ask whether any of the children have visited a botanical garden and talk about the things that they saw there.

2. Explain that Kew Gardens Museum has close to a hundred thousand species of plant and new ones are continually being added when new species are discovered. Researchers at Kew also work with people across the world on the *Useful Plants Project* so that people living in local communities can help plants in their local area to thrive and make best use of them.

3. Ask the children how many things they can think of that we utilise plants for and note these down.

Paired work

4. Tell the children that a friendly alien from the planet Zac has landed on Earth and tells you that the people who live on Zac are starving. The alien needs to know which plants are eaten here on Earth so that seeds can be taken back to Zac to provide food.

5. Ask the children to help the alien by listing:

● all the fruits they can think of
● all the vegetables they can think of
● all the cereals they can think of
● any drinks they can think of that use plants
● any herbs or spices made from plants
● any plants that are grown as food for animals.

6. Next they should pick three items from their lists, using a different list for each item, and write a report for the alien which describes:

● each item of food
● how the relevant plant grows
● the climate it grows best in
● how the food is harvested
● how the seeds of the plant are collected.

> **Differentiation**
> ● Support children who find listing herbs and spices difficult, and if necessary move on, as the more important part of the task is to write the report on what is needed for the cultivation of their choice of food.
> ● Challenge children to expand their choice of three items and set out a breakfast and lunch menu for the alien to give a balanced diet. For each food chosen they should give the background of the plant to be used.

Science in the wider world

Kew Gardens and its museums are an invaluable source worldwide, not only for knowledge of thousands of plant species, but also for their preservation.

Review

Make a list with the children of how many different fruits and vegetables they can think of and display the children's reports.

Objectives
● To understand how plants and trees make their own food.

Resources
Photocopiable page 'How plants make their own food' from the CD-ROM

Speaking scientifically
carbon, nutrients, carbon dioxide, chlorophyll, photosynthesis, minerals

Lesson 1: How plants make their own food

Introduction

Ask the children where a plant gets its food from. It is very likely that they will say *the soil*. The important point is that a plant does not get food from the soil; it makes food for itself. Explain that in some ways plants are far more clever than animals or even humans since neither of these species is capable of producing food for themselves, at least not with the help of just sunlight and water. Imagine having Sunday lunch by sitting outside with a glass of water!

Whole-class work

1. Explain that the process of a plant or tree using their leaves to create food is called photosynthesis. Green plants use light to make food through *chlorophyll* which is the green pigment in their leaves. The chlorophyll uses light and water to change carbon dioxide in the air into food for the plant and oxygen which is given back into the air.

2. This process is very important for humans and other animals since they need oxygen to survive.

3. Ask: *If plants don't get their food from the soil then how do soil and the minerals from the soil help the plant?* (They help to anchor the roots of the plant to the ground and provide nutrients to make the plant strong.)

Individual/paired work

4. Give the children photocopiable page 'How plants make their own food' from the CD-ROM and ask them to fill in the missing part of each label from the list of words given.

> **Differentiation**
> ● Support children by emphasising that plants grow through a very different process from animals. They grow their own food and they need light and water to do this.
> ● Challenge children to write down in their own words how a plant makes its own food.

Science in the wider world

Plants use sunlight to create energy or food. Scientists are trying to discover the process that plants use since it may be useful in creating low-cost energy. As yet the process involved in photosynthesis, which is complex, has not been fully solved.

Review

Check through the children's sheets with them explaining the process of photosynthesis again. Ask some members of the class to present in their own words *How plants make their own food.*

Objectives
● To learn how bulbs and tubers grow.

Resources
Some seed potatoes or potatoes that have started to sprout; egg boxes; an area of ground to plant potatoes a sprouting onion; a digital microscope or visualiser (if available); a range of bulbs, corms, rhizomes and tubers (if available)

Speaking scientifically
geophytes, bulbs, tubers, corms, rhizomes, perennial

Lesson 2: Bulbs, tubers and others

Introduction
Explain to the children that *geophytes* are the parts of plants known as bulbs, tubers, corms or rhizomes that store food for the next growing season. These plants are perennials and although they also have flowers and make seeds they store their own food underground to ensure that they will survive the non-growing season.

Bulbs contain layers of leaves and flowers; the bulb sends out roots to keep its inner leaves moist so it is ready to grow when it is warm enough. The bulb also gets larger and may produce many small bulbs each year which can be separated and grow independently of the parent plant.

Corms do not contain leaves or flowers but do store food to be used by the plant to help it grow.

Rhizomes have a horizontal stem that gets thicker so it can store food. These thick stems can often be seen above ground.

Tubers are lumps or bumps that develop on roots or underground stems to store food.

Whole-class work
1. Show the children a range of examples of bulbs, corms rhizomes and tubers.

2. Look at the sprouting onion and explain that this is a bulb; show the inside leaf structure. Cut the onion in half and point out the layers of leaves inside the bulb using a digital microscope or visualiser if you have one.

3. Stress that most bulbs are not edible and many are poisonous.

Paired work
4. Give the children a piece of egg box to put their potato in and either one potato to each pair or half a potato if each half contains an eye. Explain that potatoes are tubers.

5. Point out the eyes on the potato and explain that shoots will grow from these eyes. Explain to the class that they are going to grow potato plants so they should put their names on their egg boxes.

6. Ask the children to stand the potato in the egg box with the blunt end (with most of the eyes) pointing upwards where there is plenty of light. When the shoots are about 2cm long they are ready to plant out (which ideally should be early April).

7. Dig a trench outside about 12cm deep and plant each potato about 30cm apart with the shoots pointing upwards. Remind them to take care not to damage the shoots while planting. If planting outside is not possible then use pots or strong bin liner bags which should be at least 30cm across and 30cm deep with holes for drainage. Allow three seed potatoes per container and grow in a sunny light area.

8. When shoots appear above ground cover them with a ridge of soil so they are just covered and continue doing this until the ridge is about 15cm high and then leave them to grow into plants.

9. The potatoes should be ready to pick between June and September depending on the type of potato grown.

Science in the wider world
All geophytes need a dormant period that may be during the summer or winter. Farmers and horticulturalists need a thorough understanding of when this occurs in order to grow them.

Review
Dig up the fresh potatoes and show children how the new tubers are formed.

MSCHOLASTIC

Objectives
● To understand the requirements of plants when setting up a garden, flower bed or vegetable plot.

Resources
A selection of seeds to grow: sunflower seeds, tomato seeds, courgette or marrow seeds; nasturtium seeds; small runner bean seeds; small plastic pots or plastic cups with a hole in the bottom; an old tray to keep the pots on; larger pots if required; compost

Speaking scientifically
sunflower, tomato, courgette, marrow, nasturtium, runner bean, compost, seedling, germinate, seed leaves

Lesson 3: A gardening project

Introduction
Tell the children that they are going to carry out a gardening project. Stress that the process of gardening requires a degree of responsibility from them in order to care and tend to their plants.

Talk about some possibilities for the project:
● each child grows their own individual plant
● groups in the class have their own large pot that they care for together
● groups in the class have their own marked plot of land that they care for collaboratively.

Whole-class/paired/individual work
1. Ask children to discuss in pairs what they want to grow, and what they will need to do to ensure their plants grow strong and healthy. Get feedback from the class as to how they would proceed. Some suggestions for the process are given below:

2. After choosing their seeds suggest they label their pots with their names and note the seed name and the height the plant is expected to grow as written on the seed packet.

3. Plant the seeds in the pots using the compost and look after them appropriately.

4. When the plant is ready to be planted out or moved to a larger pot the children should do this carefully.

5. Tell children that their plant may look a little weary at this stage but that it should start to recover and that they will need to keep watering it carefully every few days, or more often if it is very sunny.

6. If group planting is envisaged then the children will need to consider putting the tallest plants at the back when they plant out and devise a rota to water their plants. If planting in a garden, then it's a good idea to separate the plots for each group with string and pegs.

Differentiation
● Support children as necessary by reminding them to water their plants.
● Challenge children to check the height of their plant every couple of days to monitor its growth and produce a chart of how their plant is growing.

Science in the wider world
Garden nurseries use a similar process for each individual plant when they produce bedding plants for the garden each spring.

Review
Ask each pair to review the success of their project. *Did the plants grow successfully? If not, at what stage did they die and why do you think this happened? How tall did the plants grow and did they flower or produce fruits or seeds?*

Objectives
● To describe the life process of reproduction in some plants and animals.

Resources
Writing materials

Working scientifically
● Presenting findings in written form, displays and other presentations.

The life story of a plant

Revise

● Remind children of the life cycle of a flowering plant.
● Plants unlike animals are fairly independent during their growth cycle.
● They can germinate with moisture and warmth as a seed has its own food and does not need light at this stage.
● The seed grows roots and shoots.
● The seedling develops seed leaves which mean the plant can start to make its own food.
● The roots take in water so that the leaves together with sunlight and carbon dioxide from the air can make food for the plant.
● The roots absorb nourishing minerals from the soil to keep it healthy.
● The seed leaves die after the plant has grown its mature leaves.
● Under the right conditions of warmth, light and moisture the plant grows a flower.
● The flower attracts insects (assuming the choice of plant is not wind-pollinated).
● The plant's bright colours and scent make the flower very attractive and the insects dig down to feed on the nectar.
● The insects get covered in pollen grains so that this reaches the stigma of the plant so it is pollinated.
● The male sex cell from a pollen grain reaches the ovary of the plant where the ovule is fertilised.
● The flower dies and leaves a fruit with seeds inside.
● The seeds are dispersed by either the wind, animals, water or the seedpod exploding.

Assess

● Tell the children that they are going to write the life story of a flowering plant of their choice from the point of view of the plant. Explain that the story should start from when they are a seed landed on the ground and finish when they are an adult plant and they have produced seeds which are dispersed ready to start a new plant.
● Tell the children to write their story in the first person and they can include drawings if they want to.

Further practice

● Children could find photographs of the different stages of the plant life cycle using the internet and arrange them in the correct order. Ask them to write a sentence to say what is happening to the plant at each stage.

Objectives
● To describe the life process of reproduction in some plants and animals.

Resources
An orchid; a cactus and a piece of seaweed; photocopiable page 'Plant adaptation' from the CD-ROM

Working scientifically
● Presenting findings in written form, displays and other presentations.

How some plants adapt to their environment

Revise

● Remind the class about the special features of orchids, cacti and seaweed which help them to survive in their habitats.
● In the rainforest, orchids:
  ● have adapted to live on the branches of other plants for support so that they can get enough light but are not parasitic
  ● have leaves that are smooth, thick and waxy to allow water to drip off easily
  ● have air roots which help the plant to absorb water and nutrients.
● In the sea, seaweed:
  ● has air bags which helps it to keep near the sea's surface or float so that it can access light;
  ● has flat leaves to get a lot of sun to produce food
  ● attaches itself to rocks or the seabed with a holdfast to help it remain underwater but these attachments do not act like a root and absorb nutrients
  ● may produce a jelly like substance to help stop them drying out.
● In the desert, a cactus:
  ● has leaves with hair to shade the plant, to reduce the heat and water loss
  ● has thick leathery leaves or even no leaves to enable it to store water;
  ● long roots that spread out wide or go deep into the ground to absorb as much water as possible when it does rain;
  ● has wide stems with a waxy coating, which may be the whole plant and which are designed to store water;
  ● has spines which help prevent animals and birds from drinking the moisture from their fleshy trunk or leaves
  ● grows slowly as this requires less energy and for the plant to make less food, reducing the amount of water it needs.

Assess

● Show the children the three plants you have brought in and give them photocopiable page 'Plant adaptation' from the CD-ROM. Tell them that they are going to write a report on each plant explaining how these plants are different from those that grow in an ordinary garden. Their task is to say how these plants are adapted to help them survive. They should say:
  ● where the plants live and what makes it difficult to survive
  ● how the roots of each plant are different and why they need to be different
  ● how the leaves are different and why this is the case.

Further practice

● Choose other plants to write about in the same way, for example bromeliads.

Objectives
● To describe the life process of reproduction in some plants and animals.

Resources
Photocopiable page 'Plant reproduction' on CD-ROM

Working scientifically
● Presenting findings in written form, displays and other presentations.

Flowers and seeds

Revise

● Remind children that seeds are formed when their flowers are fertilised after pollination. The three main parts of the plant that are involved in fertilisation are the stamen (the male part) the stigma (the female part), and the ovary (where the eggs or ovules are stored). Remind children that seeds are formed from the ovules inside the ovary which is the fruit of the plant once the plant is fertilised. Refer back to week 3, lesson 3 if necessary.

● Next discuss the following points to remind children of methods of dispersion:

● Dispersion of seeds is important because a seed may have a better chance of flourishing if it germinates well away from the parent plant.

● Discuss why this may be the case: eg more space to grow allowing more light and more water.

● Discuss different methods of dispersion and ask children for any examples they can remember. Some methods and examples are:

  ● Wind: some plants have specially designed wings to help them move further from the parent plant such as ash trees, dandelions, sycamore trees.

  ● Explosion: the seedpods burst open on plants such as gorse and lupins.

  ● Water: used by plants which grow by a stream such as foxgloves, harebells and willow and silver birch trees. Coconuts are also often dispersed by the sea.

  ● Animals: the fruits of the plant which often contain their seeds (strawberries exceptionally have their seeds on the outside) provide food for birds, animals and even humans. Animals and birds eat the seeds which may be berries from trees, strawberries or raspberries which they later excrete far away from the parent plant where the seeds start to grow. A second way animals may disperse seeds is if they have sticky surfaces; seeds may attach to the coats of animals and are later deposited on the ground. Other seeds, especially those from trees such as acorns or hazelnuts, may be buried as winter food by squirrels for example. Those nuts that are left uneaten often germinate to create a new tree.

Assess

● Ask the children to complete photocopiable page 'Plant reproduction' from the CD-ROM.

Further practice

● Ask the children to name any plants or trees that they are familiar with and say how they think their seeds are usually dispersed.

■SCHOLASTIC

Labelled flower

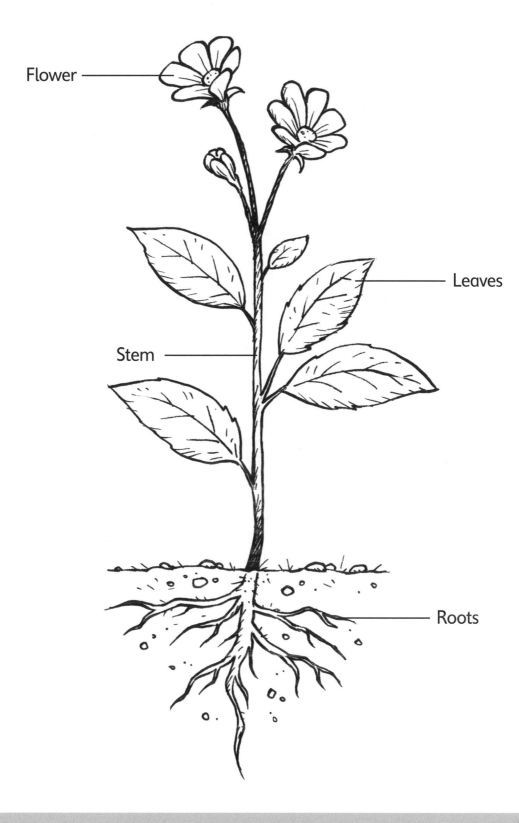

Flower

Leaves

Stem

Roots

I can recognise parts of a plant.

How did you do?

PHOTOCOPIABLE

Parts of a flower

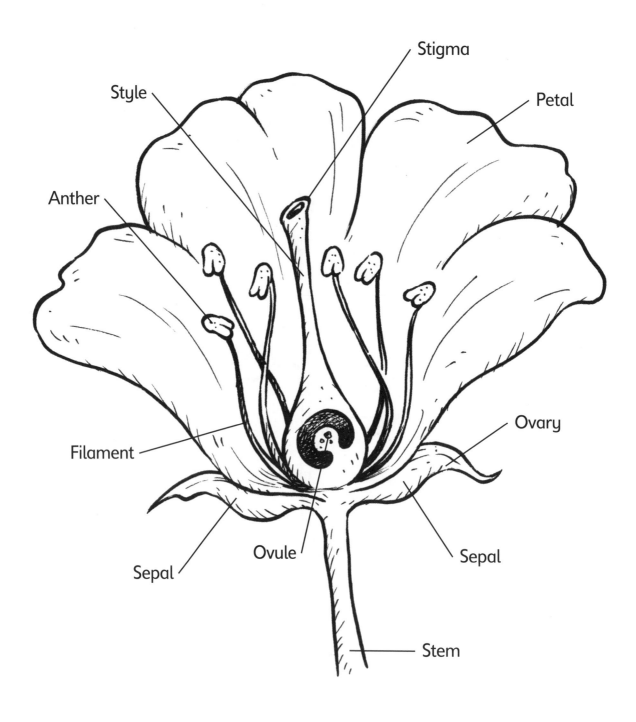

Stigma

Style

Petal

Anther

Filament

Ovary

Sepal

Ovule

Sepal

Stem

I can recognise the parts of a flower.

How did you do?

PHOTOCOPIABLE

■ SCHOLASTIC
www.scholastic.co.uk

Name: _____ Date: _____

Pollinator observation sheet

■ Part A: Find a flower or group of flowers and fill in the following details:

Date: _____ Time: _____

Temperature: _____ Weather conditions: _____

Name of flower: _____ Colour: _____

Arrangement (circle one): single flower group of flowers

Scent (circle one) mild strong

■ Draw your flower here:

Stick your strip of pollen here:

■ Part B: Tally the pollinators that visit your flower(s) over a 10-minute period.

Time: From: _____

Until: _____

Pollinator	Tally	Total
Bees		
Flies		
Wasps		
Beetles		
Butterflies		
Ants		
Others		

Write down details of any interesting or repeated behaviour you observed:

_____

_____

I can observe closely pollinators which visit flowers.

How did you do?

Seeds

Tree	Fruit or seed
Oak	Has an acorn, often found in a cup.
Sycamore	Has double-winged keys.
Holly	The red fruits are near the stalk of a prickly leaf.
Rowan	Red fruits surrounded by feathery leaves.
Ash	Has long, narrow, wing-shaped keys.
Horse chestnut	A shiny, heavy 'conker' in a prickly shell.

1. Look at how the fruits and seeds of each tree are described in the table above. Find the picture below that fits each description and write the name of the tree below it.

2. Think about the three ways that each seed could be dispersed: birds, other animals or the wind. Below each seed picture write how the seed would be dispersed.

3. Draw a cartoon creature beside each seed: a squirrel or badger next to the animal-dispersed seeds or a blackbird or song thrush next to the bird-sown seeds. Write a 'W' next to the wind-blown seeds.

Tree _____
Dispersal _____

Tree _____
Dispersal _____

Tree _____
Dispersal _____

Tree _____
Dispersal _____

Tree _____
Dispersal _____

Tree _____
Dispersal _____

I can understand different ways that seeds are dispersed.

How did you do?

PHOTOCOPIABLE

Plant life cycle

- Order these drawing by numbering each stage in the life cycle.
- Write down the name of the stage on each picture if you can.

○

_____

○

_____

○

_____

○

_____

○

_____

○

_____

I can describe the life cycle of a plant.

How did you do?

Name: _____

Date: _____

Habitats

Plants	wet	dry	sunny	shady	woodland	top of a hill
1.						
2.						
3.						
4.						

I can recognise habitats.

How did you do?

PHOTOCOPIABLE

■SCHOLASTIC
www.scholastic.co.uk

Theophrastus: true or false?

■ Here are some statements that Theophrastus made about plants over 2000 years ago. Say which you think have changed from the way scientists think about plants today (false) and which are the same (true).

■ Give reasons for your answers and use a separate piece of paper if needed.

I. Theophrastus classified plants into trees with a single woody stem, shrubs with woody stems, and herbs with soft stems. _____

2. Cultured plants are often infested with diseases, while this hardly ever occurs to wild plants. _____

3. Seeds need humidity and warmth, otherwise they will not germinate.

_____

4. Trees that grow in dense woods without sun or wind become weak.

_____

5. The growth of plants depends on the climate they are grown in and the soil.

6. Peas and beans are the same as cereals. _____

7. Tree trunks: there are great differences concerning heights and strength, composition, layering and the flake of the bark. _____

8. Flowers and leaves move during certain times of the day or year.

_____

9. The ability to germinate decreases with the age of the seeds. In general it is gone within their fourth year, though peas and beans keep it longer.

_____

10. The fruit of a plant makes it desirable as food, while the seeds inside are important for preserving the plant, which means these are conflicting processes.

_____

II. Plants growing too close to each other do not thrive due to the shortage of nutrients. _____

I can determine true and false statements.

How did you do?

Name: _____

Date: _____

Classifying plants

■ Use the key below to identify each of the plants listed and any specimens that you may have brought in.

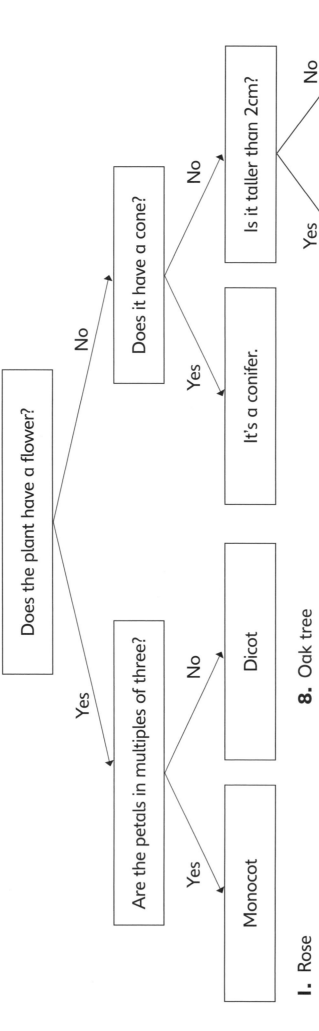

Does the plant have a flower?

Yes → Are the petals in multiples of three?

  Yes → Monocot

  No → Dicot

No → Does it have a cone?

  Yes → It's a conifer.

  No → Is it taller than 2cm?

    Yes → It's a fern.

    No → It's a moss.

1. Rose
2. Tomato
3. Daffodil
4. Christmas tree
5. Iris
6. Carnation
7. Fern
8. Oak tree
9. Specimen A
10. Specimen B
11. Specimen C
12. Specimen D
13. Specimen E

How did you do?

I can use a key to classify plants.

PHOTOCOPIABLE

Properties of materials: irreversible changes

Expected prior learning
- Understand the basic three states of matter.
- Understand that matter can change states for different reasons, such as temperature change, chemical reaction or physical manipulation.

Overview of progression
By the end of this chapter children should have learned:

- the states of matter, in particular with reference to separating mixtures in different ways
- to appreciate irreversible changes that do not need heat
- to understand and investigate the role of heat in changing foodstuffs
- to investigate the effects of burning on different materials
- to investigate vinegar and bicarbonate of soda, in particular the creation and collection of carbon dioxide
- to understand iron and the causes and effects of rust
- to understand plastics – their manufacture, properties and history.

Creative context
- Several experiments in this chapter introduce children to interesting phenomena: substances that are hard when hit but slimy when handled gently; plaster of Paris; invisible inks; making 'plastic milk' and slime. All of these present creative opportunities, particularly art, DT and literacy.
- With advanced planning there are opportunities for secret messages, hidden artefacts (in plaster of Paris); jewellery and statues; and original breads and biscuits, with the option of creating stalls to sell goods to raise funds for chosen charities.

Background knowledge
The three states of matter are defined by how active molecules are, which is easiest to envisage with ice/water/steam. Although some other materials also freeze, melt and evaporate, many do not: when they change their state it is not reversible. This is not always a bad thing – much of the modern world is based on the creation of new materials such as plastic. As such, controlling the way substances change state is the work of many scientists.

Understanding burning is critical for health and safety – we need to know the properties of solids, liquids and gasses to know how dangerous they are, and whether they can be useful in fighting fire. Although oxygen is essential to life, it is highly flammable and helps things to burn. It can also cause some materials to disintegrate, such as rusting iron, a process known as oxidisation.

Speaking scientifically
- Children will need to know the vocabulary associated with melting, dissolving, and evaporating. As the chapter progresses, words associated with irreversible change become more important, such as reaction and oxidisation.

Preparation
You will need to provide: Equipment and materials are listed for every lesson. Children will need to work alone, in pairs and in groups so you will need to have sufficient numbers of much of the equipment. Children will also need access to the internet and reference books.

On the CD-ROM you will find: photocopiable pages 'Irreversible changes that involve heat', 'Irreversible changes that do not require heat'; interactive activities 'Burning: before and after slideshow', 'Melt, boil, cool, freeze', 'Collecting carbon dioxide', 'Fizz, bang, sizzle'; media resources 'Firefighters in action', 'A volcano', 'Rusted objects'

Chapter at a glance

Week	Lesson	Curriculum objectives	Lesson objectives	Main activity	Working scientifically
1	1	• (Y4) To observe that some materials change state when they are heated or cooled, and measure or research the temperature at which this happens in degrees Celsius (°C). • To use knowledge of solids, liquids and gases to decide how mixtures might be separated, including through filtering, sieving and evaporating.	• To describe ways of separating mixtures. • To identify the factors affecting dissolving. • To identify a range of reversible changes. • To introduce the concept that some changes form new materials.	Separating salt, sand and metals. Reviewing the factors affecting dissolving. Making simple slime and considering the changes involved.	• Using simple models to describe scientific ideas. • Identifying scientific evidence that has been used to support or refute ideas or arguments.
	2	• To explain that some changes result in the formation of new materials, and that this kind of change is not usually reversible, including changes associated with burning and the action of acid on bicarbonate of soda.	• To understand the changes which take place when water and plaster of Paris are mixed.	Making a cast or mould of an object then observing and describing the events that occur when Plaster of Paris and water are mixed, then applying their knowledge.	• Using simple models to describe scientific ideas.
	3	• To explain that some changes result in the formation of new materials, and that this kind of change is not usually reversible.	• To understand how invisible ink works.	Following instructions to make and use invisible ink, then investigate the suitability of materials for use as invisible inks.	• Planning different types of scientific enquiries to answer questions, including recognising and controlling variables where necessary. • Reporting and presenting findings from enquiries.
2	1	• To explain that some changes result in the formation of new materials, and that this kind of change is not usually reversible, including changes associated with burning and the action of acid on bicarbonate of soda.	• To consider the effect of heat on a range of foods.	Planning a fair test to compare how heat affects different foods such as butter, chocolate, sugar, egg and butter, and then carry out the test following appropriate safety procedures.	• Planning different types of scientific enquiries to answer questions, including recognising and controlling variables where necessary. • Recording data and results of increasing complexity using scientific diagrams and labels, classification keys, tables, bar and line graphs.
	2	• To explain that some changes result in the formation of new materials.	• To understand the effect of heat on dough.	Following a recipe to make bread. Recording the changes in dough due to heating.	• Reporting and presenting findings from enquiries.
	3	• To explain that some changes result in the formation of new materials.	• To investigate properties of biscuits made in different proportions of ingredients and different baking times.	Make a selection of biscuits using different ingredients and/or baking conditions, then record and compare results.	• Planning different types of scientific enquiries to answer questions. • Reporting and presenting findings from enquiries.
3	1	• To explain that some changes result in the formation of new materials, and that this kind of change is not usually reversible.	• To consider the effect of burning on a range of materials.	Considering the effect of burning a variety of materials.	• Identifying scientific evidence that has been used to support or refute ideas or arguments.
	2	• To explain that some changes result in the formation of new materials, and that this kind of change is not usually reversible.	• To consider the changes that take place when a candle burns.	Observing the changes that take place when a candle burns. Interpreting results to measure the burning rate of various candles.	• Reporting and presenting findings from enquiries. • Identifying scientific evidence that has been used to support or refute ideas or arguments.
	3	• To explain that some changes result in the formation of new materials, and that this kind of change is not usually reversible, including changes associated with the action of acid on bicarbonate of soda.	• To know what happens when vinegar is added to bicarbonate. • To know the effect of the gas produced on a flame. • To understand the science behind fighting fires.	Observing and describing the changes that take place when vinegar is mixed with bicarbonate of soda. Devising a way of testing the effect of the gas on a flame. Carrying out and describing their plan.	• Using simple models to describe scientific ideas.

Chapter at a glance

Week	Lesson	Curriculum objectives	Lesson objectives	Main activity	Working scientifically
4	1	• To explain that some changes result in the formation of new materials, and that this kind of change is not usually reversible.	• To know that sometimes a gas is produced by an irreversible reaction.	Considering ways of collecting the gas produced by adding vinegar to bicarbonate of soda. Collecting a sample of gas produced by the reaction.	• Planning different types of scientific enquiries to answer questions. • Using test results to make predictions to set up further comparative and fair tests.
	2	• To explain that some changes result in the formation of new materials, and that this kind of change is not usually reversible.	• To know the effect of diluting the vinegar on its reaction with bicarbonate of soda.	Producing a series of dilutions of vinegar and predicting outcomes, then devising a fair test for measuring the effect of the dilutions and predicting the results.	• Reporting and presenting findings from enquiries. • Using test results to make predictions to set up further comparative and fair tests.
	3	• To explain that some changes result in the formation of new materials, and that this kind of change is not usually reversible, including changes associated with burning and the action of acid on bicarbonate of soda.	• To learn about the processes taking place in a volcanic eruption.	Using secondary sources to research volcanic eruptions. Using knowledge acquired to construct a model volcano. Explaining how eruptions differ between the model and a real volcano.	• Using simple models to describe scientific ideas.
5	1	• To explain that some changes result in the formation of new materials, and that this kind of change is not usually reversible.	• To learn where rusting takes place. • To consider factors that may cause rusting.	Recording observations of rusting materials. Carrying out fair tests into the causes of rusting.	• Identifying scientific evidence that has been used to support or refute ideas or arguments.
	2	• To explain that some changes result in the formation of new materials, and that this kind of change is not usually reversible.	• To know how to prevent rusting.	Considering factors which might prevent rusting. Devising an investigation into rust prevention.	• Planning different types of scientific enquiries to answer questions, including recognising and controlling variables where necessary. • Reporting and presenting findings from enquiries.
	3	• To research and discuss how chemical changes have an impact on our lives.	• To understand the processes and work involved in using iron beneficially.	Researching the manufacture, use and care of iron in manufacture and construction.	• Recognising which secondary sources will be most useful to research their ideas.
6	1	• To explain that some changes result in the formation of new materials and that this kind of change is not usually reversible. • To discuss the creative use of new materials such as polymers.	• To learn how polymers are created. • To understand the effect of temperature on the initial reaction.	Carrying out mixing, stirring and filtering in the plastic making process.	• Using simple models to describe scientific ideas.
	2	• To discuss the creative use of new materials such as polymers, super-sticky and super-thin materials.	• To investigate the properties of plastics and compare them to other materials.	Comparing different plastic objects to other materials with similar functions, such as bags.	• Planning different types of scientific enquiries to answer questions, including recognising and controlling variables where necessary. • Identifying scientific evidence that has been used to support or refute ideas or arguments.
	3	• To find out about how chemists create new materials.	• To find out about the life and work of a scientist and the impact of their discoveries.	Using secondary sources to find out about Ruth Benerito and Leo Baekerland's lives, their discoveries and the effects they had on society.	• Recognising which secondary sources will be most useful to research their ideas.
Assess and review					

Objectives
● To describe ways of separating mixtures.
● To identify the factors affecting dissolving.
● To identify a range of reversible changes.
● To introduce the concept that some changes form new materials.

Resources
Interactive activity 'Melt, boil, freeze, condense?' on the CD-ROM; sand; salt; paper clips; magnets; filter paper and funnels; water; sugar cubes; video camera (optional); mortar and pestle; heat source; glass jars; measuring spoons; cornflour; mixing bowls and stirring spoons; food colouring (optional)

Speaking scientifically
boil, condensation, condense, dissolve, evaporate, evaporation, filter, freeze, gas, liquid, molecule, solid

Lesson 1: Changes of state

Previous knowledge

Children should understand that water changes state in a 'stable' manner according to its temperature, and that these changes can be reversed by adjusting the temperature. In addition, they should know that other materials change state too, often in a reversible way. They should have experience in separating mixtures of solids, and substances like sand and salt from water.

Introduction

Open the interactive activity 'Melt, boil, freeze, condense?' on the CD-ROM and work through it with the class to reinforce concepts, conditions and vocabulary for the different states of matter.

Recap, with a particular focus on water, how matter can change states. Discuss and model how the molecules behave in each state: tightly-packed, ordered and rigid for solids, looser and moving for liquids, and free-moving uninhibited and expansive for gases.

Ask what the children understand by *reversible change*, and elicit two key factors: some materials can change from solid to liquid or liquid to gas and back again without losing their inherent properties (whereas others cannot); also, when some substances are mixed with a different substance they also change (such as sugar dissolving in water), but nevertheless they can be recovered – in other words some mixtures are also reversible.

Whole-class work

1. Begin with a mixture of sand, salt and paper clips (or something similar) and challenge the children to explain how they would separate the three components.

2. Working individually, ask them to write down the different procedures and in which order they would perform them. (They should use a magnet to remove the paper clips first of all, then add water to the sand and salt, stir and then filter to remove the sand. They should leave the filtrate somewhere warm, allowing the water to evaporate leaving salt crystals behind.)

3. Discuss the children's thoughts and ideas, reinforcing correct vocabulary and stressing the need for methodical working.

4. Next, with the whole class focused, explain that you have a sugar cube and you want to dissolve it in water as quickly as possible. In discussion, build up two lists: one of ideas for what to do, the other for equipment needed to dissolve the sugar.

5. After a while review the lists and ask the class to agree on a process that will be the quickest.

6. Test one or more processes, timing the outcome. (If possible set up a video camera next to the experiment to view it larger on your whiteboard.) The possible actions include: grinding the sugar from cube to grains, using warm or hot water and stirring the mixture.

7. Once the sugar has dissolved discuss what has happened. Establish that the sugar has been incorporated into the water, and consider why the actions taken might help. If appropriate, consider how the process could be further speeded up.

8. Finally, discuss what reversible changes the children are already aware of. Talk about the different states of water and how it moves between them, both in nature (the water cycle, the changing polar ice-caps) and its uses in our daily lives (industry, refrigeration, and so on).

Introducing the new area of study

Explain that you would like children to do a small investigation into mixing cornflour with water. Stressing that they do not have to mix large quantities each time, ask groups to investigate what happens when the two are mixed and how changing quantities of flour changes the composition and properties of the mixture.

Demonstrate how they might measure quantities of the two and mix them (ideally using glass or plastic jars). Demonstrate a suitable format for recording their findings.

Distribute the materials (adding food colourings to the water before mixing the cornflour gives a wow factor, as well as making it easier for children to colour code their results chart).

Ask the groups to note in particular the points at which the water starts to feel and behave differently, and to consider if there is a point beyond which adding further cornflour has no effect.

While the children are working (or beforehand), prepare a bowl of water and cornflour. If you mix it to the correct amounts you will have a substance that appears to be hard when hit, but is slimy and runny when you carefully dip your fingers into it. (This is because the cornflour particles are suspended in the water and therefore flow like a liquid. However, when force is applied the particles lock together and act like a solid, but go back to being a liquid when the force is removed.)

> **Differentiation**
> ● Allow children who need support to have a very tactile experience with their mixtures (you are never too old!).
> ● Challenge children to try and explain what is happening, and why the process cannot be reversed. Also, when they have found an ideal mixture, can they extrapolate what quantities of water and cornflour would be needed for large-scale production (such as a gallon).

Science in the wider world

Many materials, such as paper, plastics, some metals and foodstuffs, are manufactured through mixing different substances in a controlled way,

In addition, some rocks are transformed when temperatures become so high that they change their chemical structures, creating new rocks and minerals.

Review

Gather the class together, and ensuring that all mess has been cleared up, ask the groups to explain their results and their findings. Focus in particular on the words used to describe the different consistencies of cornflower and water. *What was it like when very little flour was added, contrasted with very large amounts of flour?*

Explain that you want to create good-quality slime, and ask the children to consider what would be the ideal proportion of cornflour to water to create this.

To conclude, display your own bowl of cornflour slime and demonstrate the effect mentioned above, whereby it behaves like a solid when a force is applied to it. Discuss why this might be happening.

Explain that what has happened to the water and the cornflour is an *irreversible change* – in other words you cannot get the original water or cornflour back again.

If you can handle a bit of mess, taking your bowl of cornflour mixture that hardens on impact, challenge the children to make it into a ball and throw it to a classmate before it turns back into slime!

Resources
Plaster of Paris; water; mixing bowls and stirrers; safety equipment: over-shirts; goggles; gloves; clay and/or polystyrene plates; internet access

Speaking scientifically
exothermic, gypsum, plaster

Lesson 2: Plaster of Paris

Introduction

Reinforce health and safety rules and procedures. Explain to the class that in this lesson and those to follow a range of materials will be used that can cause problems if they are not used properly. In addition, some of the lessons involve heating materials, which again should have a clear set of procedures and rules attached to them.

Explain that in this lesson everyone will be using plaster of Paris – a fine powder made from gypsum, which, when mixed with water sets quite quickly. Draw close attention to the fact that plaster is exothermic, meaning it generates heat as it sets. Note also that it is difficult to get it off skin, and contact should be avoided. (You may also want to do this as a supervised carousel activity.)

Paired work

1. Demonstrate roughly how much plaster will be allocated to each group (ideally, show them a plaster object you have prepared in advance to illustrate the scale of the envisaged work), and look at the clay or polystyrene plates available for mould-making.

2. Before the children start working, explain that as plaster of Paris is made by heating gypsum to remove the water in it, by adding water they are in effect restoring it to its original state. Point out that they will need to ensure the plaster and water are well mixed to form a smooth, consistent solution.

3. Once the children's moulds are made (either by moulding clay or pressing linear designs into the polystyrene plates) they can mix and then pour their plaster. As they do so ask: *Why does the plaster set at room temperature? What has happened to the water?*

4. Once their plaster has dried, carefully remove the moulds and consider the finished pieces.

> **Differentiation**
> ● Support children by allowing them to watch the setting process closely, explaining to them how adding water is in effect returning the plaster to its original state.
> ● Challenge more confident children to research how plaster of Paris is made, and where its name comes from (interestingly, it is made by heating gypsum to remove the water, but it is recommended that you do not investigate whether the process is reversible once children have made their artefacts).

Science in the wider world

There are other types of plaster, lime and cement, which are used in construction work. Plaster is also used in complex details in interiors, typically on ceilings using moulds, as well as for statues (alabaster is a type of gypsum). Plaster expands as it sets; it is well-suited to moulds. It has been used for a long time – there is evidence that the Ancient Egyptians and Romans used it. Because it contains moisture it has some uses in fire protection. As every unfortunate person who has broken an arm or leg knows, it is ideal for making casts to support and protect broken bones as they heal by covering bandages with it.

Review

Gather the class and discuss what they have learned in the lesson, as well as evaluating their health and safety practice. Give everyone the opportunity to examine each others' work, and if desired, allow further time for children to compete and enhance their creations.

Objectives
● To understand how invisible ink works.

Resources
A stereotypical spy outfit (optional); a selection of juices; milk and vinegar; sugar and salt; water; dipping or fountain pens; writing paper; a suitable source of heat; video camera (optional); internet access (optional)

Speaking scientifically
acid, burn, oxidise, oxidisation

Lesson 3: Secret messages

Introduction

Try to start the lesson in role as a spy, hamming it up as much as you can. Explain to the children that you are in need of a good system for passing secret messages in a way that no one will suspect. Say that you have heard that it is possible to make invisible ink (some of the children may know this too). Tell them that you want them to create the best invisible ink of all.

State that all you know is that some spies are able to take blank sheets of paper, hold them near something that is fairly hot, and hey-presto, writing appears! Say that you want to know how to do it, and how to make sure your enemies do not see anything suspicious, even when they hold paper up to the light.

As a final flourish, demonstrate this with a piece of paper you have prepared earlier, perhaps with a dramatic message on it.

Group or paired work

Reminding the children of the need for consistency to obtain meaningful results, ask them to plan their tests. Give them free reign to experiment (though it is suggested that you control the heat sources; you will need to test and plan these in advance – radiators or light bulbs may provide enough heat).

Once a range of substances have been tested remind the children that the challenge is to find the perfect *ink*, and to consider how they might modify the basic ingredients. Encourage them to experiment with different dilutions and mixtures.

Insist that their method and results are carefully recorded alongside a brief report explaining their recommendations.

Differentiation
● To provide help for those who cannot grasp the processes involved, allow them plenty of opportunities to watch the phenomenon close up (video it for replay if this is safer).
● Challenge children to research different types of invisible inks and the procedures or reactions that are needed to reveal them. *Which ones are the easiest to use? Which are the most effective?*

Science in the wider world

As well as inks that appear when heated, there are inks that can appear through chemical reaction and ultraviolet light, and even inks that disappear over time. Although its use is now decreasing, invisible ink was for many years a popular tool for spies all over the world, and security firms still use special invisible inks to mark money and goods that are at risk.

Review

Gather the class and discuss their work, noting who has successfully identified suitable substances (although lemon juice is best known, other substances also work). Look in particular at any unusual ideas, and decide who has created the most undetectable ink that also delivers clearly legible writing when heated.

Note also groups who have worked methodically and recorded results accurately and effectively, perhaps rating *ink quality* out of ten.

Finally, explain that when heated some substances oxidise (they turn brown), and this phenomena allows the creation of invisible ink.

Objectives
● To consider the effect of heat on a range of foods.

Resources
A slice of bread and a slice of (unbuttered) toast; a raw egg and a boiled egg; a knife, a range of foods suitable for heating; such as milk, eggs, chocolate and butter; a suitable heat source; such as a portable electric hob; plates; glass bowls; a whisk or fork; pans, ideally see-through; thermometers (optional); a video camera (optional); photocopiable page 168 'Heating foods'

Speaking scientifically
heat, change of state, reversible and irreversible change

Lesson 1: Heating foods

Introduction
With the children gathered around you, begin the lesson with two plates in front of you. Place a slice of bread and a raw egg on one plate, and a slice of toast and a hard-boiled egg on the other (it may help to make a mark the hard-boiled egg to help you remember which is which). Hold up the bread and the toast, passing them round if desired. Discuss the differences in their appearance and their properties (the toast will probably be darker, the bread floppier). Ask what might cause these differences. Establish that the toast has been heated. *Has anyone ever seen toast heated for too long? What happens?*

Next, look at the eggs, and perform the spin test. (If an egg is cooked it will spin smoothly, but if it is raw it will wobble erratically when spun – due to the fluid moving around.)

Crack both the eggs over a glass bowl. Look at the composition of the uncooked egg and contrast it with the hard-boiled egg (cut this in half to reveal the yolk).

To conclude, whisk the uncooked egg and ask the children to consider and explain what has happened.

Group work
1. Display photocopiable page 168 'Heating foods' and discuss how this would be completed for heating bread.

2. Arrange the class into small groups and give each one the photocopiable sheet. Reviewing the different equipment and foods available to them, ask the children to plan and perform a small range of tests for three to four foods of their choice.

3. Before they start working, remind them of the essentials of health and safety. None of the foodstuffs should be consumed, and if heating sources are being used without direct adult supervision they should not be dangerous (using bowls placed in warm water may be enough to heat some of the substances).

Differentiation
● Group children accordingly and allow those who need support to have as much observational and hands-on experience as possible, providing them with key words and/ or pictures to help them complete their charts.
● More confident children could use thermometers (or research) to provide more accurate information about melting points.

Science in the wider world
Understanding the properties of foods is important for everyday living. We need to know what we can do with foods to create healthy and enjoyable meals. Eating foods that are uncooked or under-heated can be dangerous, such as some meat and fish.

All foods change if they are overheated, and although not necessarily bad for you, they are usually unpleasant to eat. Overcooking food can often destroy any nutritional value, and some research suggests that eating burnt foods can increase the risk of cancer.

Review
Gather the class and discuss their findings. Through questioning, encourage the children to consider why some foods, like chocolate, melt with heating, whereas others, like eggs, solidify.

Repeating tests for everyone to see if necessary, reconsider foods that appear to have reversible changes, such as chocolate and butter. Ask the children to decide if they are identical to their original state after undergoing heating and cooling, or whether they are different.

Objectives
● To understand the effect of heat on dough.

Resources
A pre-baked; uncut loaf; kitchen utensils; baking facilities; bread flour; easy-use yeast; water; salt; photocopiable page 169 'Baking bread'

Speaking scientifically
carbon dioxide, change of state, irreversible change, reaction

Lesson 2: Baking bread

Introduction
Display an uncut loaf of bread for everyone to see. Make a show of cutting it in half and examine the insides, considering how it varies from the outside. Try to elicit ideas for what gives the loaf its texture.

Keeping the loaf visible, show the class each of the ingredients needed for making bread. Encourage them to ponder how they could be transformed from their raw states into the loaf now before them.

Whole-class work
1. The main part of the lesson is a demonstration of preparing and baking bread or rolls. As such it may have to take place over several sessions, ideally all in the same day. If you do not have the facilities for baking you can still demonstrate the mixing, rising and kneading processes, using the loaf from the introduction to demonstrate, compare and examine the finished product. The approach you take to this part of the lesson will depend on the time and facilities available to you. Ideally, demonstrate how to mix the basic ingredients, watch the yeast rise, prepare the loaf or rolls, then bake and examine them.

2. As you prepare the bread talk to the class about the process:
● Strong flour is used because it bonds together better and makes a better dough.
● Yeast is added because it reacts with the dough and gives off carbon dioxide, making the dough expand and rise.
● The amount of water added is very important – changing it will make the dough thinner or thicker, producing different types of bread.
● Kneading the dough makes it smoother and more elastic, so it is easier to manipulate and shape.
● The dough needs time to rise, usually around one to two hours, and then has to be *knocked* back to remove any gas that has formed. It is then shaped into a loaf before putting into the oven.
● As heat destroys yeast, the loaf will not rise much more in the oven.

Independent work
3. Give each child a copy of photocopiable page 169 'Baking bread'. Ask them to arrange the instructions in the correct order then explain what happens when bread is made.

Differentiation
● Allow children who find writing hard just to arrange the instructions, and if appropriate to illustrate each one.
● For a more challenging task, invite the children to arrange the instructions with gaps between them, then write a short paragraph under each one to explain why this is done or what is happening.

Science in the wider world
There are many different types of bread, formed not only by adding different flours and yeasts, but also ingredients. Whole books are written to explain how different variations can be made, varying cooking times as well as ingredients. Much of the bread we purchase from shops is baked in large batches, where quality and consistency is a combination of human skill and complex machinery. A baker's dozen (13) is named thus because in the past the extra loaf was used to check quality.

Review
Ask the class to share their work with each other, in particular asking them to look for partners' use of scientific vocabulary.

Objectives
● To investigate properties of biscuits made in different proportions of ingredients and different baking times.

Resources
Three types of biscuits (none coated in chocolate; one plain and simple); a collection of biscuit wrappers for examining ingredients; a range of ingredients for making savoury and/or sweet biscuits; kitchen utensils; baking facilities; a range of biscuit cookbooks (optional); internet access (optional)

Speaking scientifically
change of state, irreversible change, reaction

Lesson 3: Making biscuits

Introduction
Arrange a variety of biscuits for the class to look at, stressing the importance of hygiene – because lots of people will be handling the sample biscuits no one should eat any part of one. Discuss the appearance and textures of each biscuit.

Next, refer to the wrappers of the biscuits (you may have to write these on your whiteboard). Ask the class to identify the different ingredients in each one and to note when they notice ingredients that are also in bread (as in the previous lesson). In particular, ask them to note additives that would not be used in home-baking.

Consider what makes basic biscuits different from bread (although they are made from dough, they have no yeast and are unleavened).

Group work
1. In small groups, explain that the children's task is to research and plan a biscuit which they might then make depending on your facilities.

2. Show (or list) a limited range of ingredients that you have available for groups to use, as well as the equipment.

3. Now the important bit – as well as making a particular sort of biscuit, explain that you want each group to choose an area of *research*, an ingredient or condition that they will vary in order to examine its effect (such as more flour, less sugar, thinner biscuits, and so on). Explain that to achieve this each group will be making three to five biscuits, with a slight variation in ingredients between each one.

4. If desired, allow the children access to cookbooks and the internet to investigate simple recipes.

5. In preparing their plans, ask each group to remember what constitutes a fair test, as well as making predictions as to what they expect to find out.

Differentiation
● Group children so that those who need support can contribute appropriately, ensuring suitable rules for groups to make decisions.
● To challenge groups, ask them to research the changes that take place in ingredients when baking biscuits, and use these facts to try and plan a more meaningful and productive test.

Science in the wider world
The word biscuit comes from Latin and French, and means *cooked twice*, as was the original approach to making biscuits. Traditionally they were a common food for the poor, made using basic ingredients in the cooling ovens once bread had been baked.

Early sailors made good use of biscuits: they stayed fresh longer than bread and took up less space, and were a convenient way of providing nutrition for sailors.

Review
The focus of your review will depend on whether or not you have been able to make the children's biscuits. If biscuits have been made, look at successes and failures, and identify why different things have happened. *Was the temperature important?* Also consider whether any of the ingredients could be separated, or if this change is also irreversible.

If the biscuits were not made, ask the groups to share their planned ingredients and baking times with each other. Discuss what they expect the biscuits to taste like, what sort of texture they will have, and so on.

Objectives
● To consider the effect of burning on a range of materials.

Resources
Large matches; wooden tapers; materials to burn (if possible); heat resistant mat; safety equipment for the teacher; photocopiable page 170 'Burning materials'; media resource 'Burning: before and after' on the CD-ROM

Speaking scientifically
burning, carbon, combustion, reaction, oxygen

Lesson 1: Burning materials

Introduction
Explain that in this session you will be burning some materials. Run through health and safety procedures with the class.

With the children gathered round, but at a safe distance, take a box of matches and a wooden taper. Explain that you intend to burn the taper, and elicit what you will do to make this happen. Rub the taper along the rough side of the matchbox. *Why won't it light?* Then strike a match and watch the end ignite, then the wood of the match burning. Explain that matches contain phosphorous which is very flammable; the friction of rubbing the match generates enough heat to ignite the phosphorous. (If appropriate, ask children to rub their hands together to see how easily friction generates heat.)

Finally, with a match lit, set a taper alight and ask the children to observe the smoke. When it has burned out, look at what remains of both the match and the taper. Establish that burning is an irreversible change, and it is often called 'combustion'. *Does anyone know what has happened to the wood? What was the smoke made of?* (See below.)

Whole-class work
1. Tell the children that you are going to be burning a small range of materials (or looking at images of them before they are burned), and that there are two halves to this session.

2. Give each child a copy of 'Burning materials' and reveal the materials to be burned, allowing children to look closely at them and touch them if possible.

3. Once everyone has written down their observations and predictions on the photocopiable sheet, burn the materials (or show images of them after they were burned, as available in the media resource 'Burning: before and after' on the CD-ROM). Ask the children to complete their photocopiable sheets.

Differentiation
● Allow children who are struggling with the concepts to touch and investigate the burned matches and taper once they have cooled. Ask why they cannot turn them back to the original material.
● To challenge children, remind them that when a material burns it usually combines with the oxygen in the air. Ask them to write a sentence for each material, suggesting what has happened.

Science in the wider world
Burning is an irreversible reaction (heating can cause reversible and irreversible reactions). When materials burn they react with the oxygen in the air to produce a new material, usually called an oxide. Fuels like wood, coal and oil produce carbon dioxide when they burn because they have carbon in them. Oil and wood are hydrocarbons, meaning they also contain hydrogen; burning them also produces water.

Burning is also called *combustion*. When carbon dioxide and water are formed they go into the atmosphere. They cannot be converted back into the original material and oxygen. Combustion is an irreversible chemical reaction.

A fuel is a material that has energy *locked up* in it. Most fuels are carbon-based *fossil fuels* such as coal, oil and natural gas. During combustion, the energy in a fuel is *unlocked* to provide energy for personal use, such as lighting, heating, cooking and for industrial use, such as transport and machinery.

Review
With a partner, ask the children to compare their work and consider similar and differing responses. Then work together to discuss each material in turn.

Ask whether the children can explain why some materials did not combust. Establish that the temperature was simply not hot enough.

Objectives
● To consider the changes that take place when a candle burns.

Resources
Safety matches; a small lock of hair; small fire-proof container; string; candles of different shapes and sizes; heat-resistant mat; a candle snuffer

Speaking scientifically
capillary action, combustion, fuel, vapourise

Lesson 2: How fast does a candle burn?

Introduction

Place a small lock of human hair in a suitable container. Ensuring everyone is safely seated and that your equipment is appropriate, use a match to light the hair (note that it burns very quickly and can give off quite a smell). Discuss why this happens, and the importance of not putting our heads near candles. Remind everyone that even birthday cake candles can be dangerous to loose hair.

Next, safely light a short length of string, watch it burn, and consider the burnt remains. Then, lighting a candle and watching it together, consider why the string does not burn so quickly. Explain how candles work (see below).

Whole-class work

1. Display a range of candles, ideally of differing thicknesses and length (though each candle should be the same thickness throughout). Create a chart on your whiteboard with a column for each candle, giving each one a name and, ideally, writing down the cost of each one.

2. Measure the length of each candle and record all the information in the first row on your whiteboard. Then safely light them all. (NB: as candles can burn slowly, you could set up this activity at the start of the day and return to it regularly, arranging the follow-up work at a separate time.)

3. After an hour or so, extinguish all of the candles. When they have cooled down, measure them again, recording the results on your whiteboard.

4. Repeat this process over several hours to generate a good range of data.

Independent or paired work

5. With all of the data clearly displayed on your whiteboard, and the unlit candles still visible (if anything remains), ask children to plan and create a brief analysis of the candles, considering the following prompts:

● Can you calculate the different rates at which the candles burned?
● Which candle is the best/worst value for money?
● Can you think of a good use for each candle?
● Can you plot graphs to show candle burning speeds?

Differentiation
● To support children, work with them to show how a graph can be plotted.
● Challenge more confident children to plan how they would choose and use a candle to tell the time.

Science in the wider world

Candles are a most ingenious invention. They burn because the heat from the wick melts the wax which moves up the wick due to capillary action; it is then vapourised by the heat of the flame. The vapour then reacts with the oxygen in the surrounding air and burns.

Candles can be made from many substances, including animal fat products (tallow), beeswax, and even whale blubber. Modern candles tend to be made from paraffin wax, which comes from oil.

Historically, candles were very important. They provided useful and reliable light and warmth, and were even used as clocks.

Review

Ask pairs of children who have worked together to team up with other pairs and share their work and conclusions. Where interpretations differ greatly, ask the children to consider the source of possible errors.

Bring everyone together and look at good interpretations of the data, using them to answer the questions you posed. Take a vote on the preferred candle.

Objectives
- To know the changes that take place when vinegar is added to bicarbonate.
- To know the effect of the gas produced on a flame.
- To understand the science behind the techniques of fighting fires.

Resources
Bicarbonate of soda; vinegar; heat-resistant glass bowl and jug; candles; matches; heat-resistant mat; media resource 'Fire-fighters in action' on the CD-ROM; video camera (optional)

Speaking scientifically
carbon dioxide, gas, hazards, non-flammable, oxygen

Introduction
Carefully mix bicarbonate of soda and vinegar in a jug, explaining that the reaction taking place is producing a gas that the children may not be able to see.

Place a small candle in a bowl and light it, eliciting the reasons why the candle is burning. If possible set up a video camera to record events.

Carefully move the jug containing the bicarbonate of soda and vinegar against the side of the bowl. Slowly tip the jug as if pouring a precious liquid, but ensure that none of the bicarbonate or the vinegar come out. (You may need to practise this beforehand.) The candle should extinguish quite quickly.

Discuss what has happened. Establish that the reaction between the bicarbonate and the vinegar produces the gas carbon dioxide. Explain that it is different from air in two key respects: firstly, it is heavier, hence it can be poured; secondly, it is not flammable. As the carbon dioxide replaces the air around the candle, the flame is starved of oxygen and stops burning.

Whole-class work
1. Show the class the media resource 'Firefighters in action' on the CD-ROM.

2. Discuss what they are doing, and how they put fires out as well as prevent them from spreading.

3. Discuss what firefighters use to stop fires: water, foam, sand and beaters:
   - water cools things down, so can stop them burning. It can also stop them catching fire at all, which is why firefighters often soak objects like trees and buildings next to a fire to stop it spreading
   - foam, like carbon dioxide, starves the fire of oxygen and extinguishes it (fire extinguishers contain foam, not water)
   - sand is useful to quickly cut off the oxygen supply to a flame
   - beaters can be useful for small fires, especially outdoors where dry grass and bushes can easily burn, with winds helping fires to spread quickly.

4. Point out the safety measures firefighters use: breathing equipment, fire-retardant suits and helmets, and good communications equipment.

Group work
Ask the children to prepare a simple presentation which explains the basics of firefighting, in particular explaining how fires can be extinguished.

Differentiation
- Group children appropriately so that some can act or show diagrams while others offer explanations.
- To challenge children's thinking, provide groups with a small section of a map of a town. Tell them there is a fire in a particular location, and ask them to imagine the measures and actions the local fire brigade would put in place.

Science in the wider world
The great fire of London in 1666 was a disaster waiting to happen: lots of wooden buildings, minimal health and safety standards, basic firefighting equipment, and a windy day. No wonder so many buildings were lost.

Nowadays large-scale fires are usually restricted to industrial disasters and countries that are very hot and dry. During the hotter months in Australia there are frequent bush fires that can cover huge areas of land, often moving quickly. Although they are very dangerous for people, ultimately such fires often help nature to regenerate more effectively than waiting for vegetation to die off.

Review
Gather the children's presentations, correcting errors if needs be, and noting good use of vocabulary and well-explained concepts.

Objectives
• To know that sometimes a gas is produced by an irreversible reaction.

Resources
Bicarbonate of soda; vinegar; a selection of collecting jars; stoppers; syringes; test tubes and tubing; safety goggles; over-shirts and gloves; matches and tapers; heat-resistant mat; heat-resistant glass bowl and jug; video of the carbon dioxide experiment from the previous lesson (optional)

Speaking scientifically
carbon dioxide, density, non-flammable, reaction

Lesson 1: Collecting gas

Introduction
Recap on the key vocabulary involved in generating carbon dioxide: chemical reaction; non-reversible change, non-flammable. If possible, watch the video made of the previous lesson's experiment mixing vinegar with bicarbonate of soda to produce carbon dioxide. While the children watch, recap on the facts involved: namely, that carbon dioxide is heavier than air, and is not flammable. Also remind children that the chemical reaction when vinegar and bicarbonate of soda interact is a non-reversible change.

Group work
1. Display the range of equipment available and discuss the safety issues. If you have limited equipment, it may be better to operate this experiment on a carousel basis.

2. Arrange the children in small groups and ask them to plan an experiment where they will try to collect a sample of carbon dioxide.

3. Ask them to consider how they will achieve this without making too much mess or losing any carbon dioxide, and how they will test that their method has worked.

4. Ask each group to write up their approach, rationale and outcomes, including a diagram of their apparatus.

5. Finally, ask them to say what they would do differently next time.

Differentiation
• Support children by allowing them freedom to watch the experiments closely and observe reactions. Also, provide a diagram for how the gas might be collected, and ask them to trace the route of the gas whilst explaining stages.
• Challenge children to consider (and/or research) how they would safely collect a gas (like hydrogen or ammonia) that is lighter than air, ensuring that none is lost.

Science in the wider world
Although we are all used to being surrounded by air which has no discernible properties, we should be very mindful that other gases can be much more dangerous and volatile. For example, carbon monoxide is a poisonous gas that can be produced by heaters and cooking equipment and is very difficult to detect. It can seriously injure or kill people if inhaled. Many homes are now fitted with suitable detectors. As gases have a range of everyday and industrial uses, it is important to be able to create, collect and store them safely. Although liquids are often used as barriers, this is only effective if the gas does not react with the liquid.

Review
Gather the class and ask which groups were successful in their experiments. Stress that if experiments did not work it is not a problem – the main thing is to try and understand why. Discuss problems and elicit explanations.

Note that the hard thing for children to appreciate is the *displacement* of the air – the denser carbon dioxide will push the air out of the jar, into the tube and then into the test tube. Stress that there would have to be a gap between the test tube and its cover to allow displaced air to escape.

To conclude, reinforce the fact that carbon dioxide is heavier than air, and as such it is *denser* – there is more carbon dioxide in a test tube full of it than there would be of air.

Lesson 2: Investigating acid strength

Objectives
● To know the effect of diluting the vinegar on its reaction with bicarbonate of soda.

Resources
Concentrated fruit juice (ideally red in colour); bicarbonate of soda; vinegar; measuring cylinders for small amounts of fluid; measuring spoons; a selection of collecting jars; water; stoppers; syringes; test tubes and tubing; safety goggles; over-shirts and gloves; video of the carbon dioxide experiment from the previous lesson (optional); visualise/webcam/video camera (optional)

Speaking scientifically
acetic acid, carbon dioxide, density, dilution, reaction

Introduction

Ask who likes chips (in moderation, of course). Also: *Who likes salt on them? Who likes ketchup?* Finally ask: *Does anyone like acid on their chips?*

Explain that vinegar contains a type of acid, called acetic acid (vinegar is roughly 10% acid and 90% water), and that acids can react with other materials, often corroding them.

Next, measure and add a small amount of juice concentrate to a glass, allowing everyone to look at it closely and consider its colour (if you have a visualiser or a webcam/video camera that will allow you to magnify it so much the better). Using measuring equipment, add a small amount of water to the concentrate, explaining that this is a slight dilution. Stir the mixture thoroughly and discuss any changes of colour.

Continue measuring and adding the same amount of water until the dilution of the juice becomes more obvious. Confirm that the glass now contains water diffused with juice concentrate, which has been diluted.

Group work

1. Recap on the previous experiments for collecting carbon dioxide. Ask the children to consider how they might set up an experiment that allows them to measure the amount of carbon dioxide generated by mixing vinegar and bicarbonate of soda. *Is it possible?*

2. Display the range of equipment available and discuss safety issues. If the equipment is limited it may be better to operate this on a carousel basis.

3. In small groups, ask the children to plan an experiment where they will try to measure the effect on the amount of gas created by mixing different dilutions of vinegar (acetic acid) with fixed amounts of bicarbonate of soda.

4. Ask them to consider how they will achieve this without making too much mess, ensuring a fair test, and how they might confirm that their method has worked.

5. Invite each group to write up their approach, rationale and outcomes, including a diagram of their apparatus and a table of results and a graph, with conclusions explaining what their results tell them (if anything).

Differentiation
● Allow children who need support to practise using measuring equipment for mixing vinegar and water, and to consider their results verbally.
● For a greater challenge, ask groups to extrapolate meaning from their results, such as explaining what amounts of carbon dioxide smaller dilutions (or stronger concentrates) of acid might generate.

Science in the wider world

Acids have many uses in industry, such as removing rust and other corrosion from metals. Sulphuric acid is used in car batteries, and stronger acids are used for processing minerals and creating fertilizers.

Some processed foods contain phosphoric and carbonic acids to preserve them – most people know about the dangers this poses for tooth decay. However, foods also contain natural acids, such as citric acid. Indeed, the human body requires a complex balance of various acids to remain healthy.

Review

Gather the class and discuss the experiment. Consider what made it a difficult task and where errors might have crept into their work. Ask if the data generated is meaningful, and what it suggests to them.

To conclude, ask groups to discuss and share what they would do differently next time, and/or what their next steps in the investigation could be.

Objectives
● To learn about the processes taking place in a volcanic eruption.

Resources
Media resource 'Volcano' on the CD-ROM; bicarbonate of soda; vinegar; modelling clay; measuring spoons; a selection of jars; safety goggles; over-shirts and gloves; newspapers for soaking up spillages; video camera; photocopiable page 171 'Volcanoes'; books and internet access (optional)

Speaking scientifically
eruption, lava, mantle, pressure

Lesson 3: A model volcano

Introduction
Show the children the media resource 'Volcano' on the CD-ROM, and discuss the different aspects with the class, ensuring that they understand the essential aspects and processes, namely that the inside of the Earth is so hot that the rock, called magma, is molten. Gaps in the solid crust allow it to come to the surface, where the pressure eventually causes it to erupt, often showering molten rock, gas and ash high into the air.

Explain that volcanoes come in many shapes and sizes, including underwater ones. The typical cone-shaped volcano is the result of many eruptions over a long period of time, where the molten rock is pushed out of the volcano then runs down the sides and cooling to form new rock.

Group work
1. It may be preferable to do this experiment as a carousel activity. Ideally, allow each group to video their experiment so that these can be replayed in the review section.

2. Show the children the materials available to them. Explain that you want them to plan, build and test a model that can be used to roughly demonstrate how a volcano works. Emphasise that the eruptions they create must be controlled and not chaotic. Children may well have encountered or performed this experiment in the past, so it is important that they think carefully about the structure of their model and the quantities of ingredients used.

Independent work
3. Give each child a copy of photocopiable page 171 'Volcanoes' and ask the children to complete it. Let them have access to books and/or the internet to aid their research, if necessary.

Differentiation
● Once again, for children who need support, the visual nature of this experiment provides a solid opportunity for understanding the processes involved. Provide key vocabulary on cue cards to help with write-ups.
● For a more challenging task, ask a group to plan a series of experiments where they can control the force of the explosion, either through mixing different dilutions of vinegar and bicarbonate and/or adjusting the structure of their clay model.

Science in the wider world
Volcanic eruptions can be very bad news for life on Earth. Some eruptions believed to have happened hundreds of thousands of years ago would have left the skies black with ash for some time, heating the planet and destroying life. Smaller eruptions, such as Pompeii in ancient Rome, and Mount St Helens in America, are just as deadly. People may be killed, with towns and huge areas of land destroyed. But they are not all bad; people often live near volcanoes as the ash can make the soil very good for growing crops, and many volcanoes are tourist attractions, such as the Thrihnukagigur Volcano in Iceland where you can actually go into a volcano!

Review
Regroup the class and, if possible, watch the videos of their model eruptions. Referring to their written work, ask the children to explain what the different parts of their models represent. *How effective is your model? What are its shortcomings?*

■ SCHOLASTIC

Objectives
- To learn where rusting takes place.
- To consider factors that may cause rusting.

Resources
Media resource 'The effects of rust' on the CD-ROM; five glass jars; iron nails; steel pins or clips; pieces of aluminium foil; plastic and wood; water (tap and distilled/boiled); packets of silica gel; paraffin (if possible); digital camera (optional)

Speaking scientifically
distilled water, iron, oxidise, rust, steel, reaction

Lesson 1: Understanding rust

Introduction

Show the children the media resource 'The effects of rust' on the CD-ROM. Discuss examples of rust that they have seen in real life. Consider what has rusted, and what the objects have in common. *Do you know why they have rusted?*

Explain that rusting is the change (or corrosion) of iron to iron oxide. This also happens to steel, as this is made from iron. It is important to understand that for rusting to occur water and oxygen are both needed: iron in dry air or water that is free of dissolved oxygen (distilled water) will not rust.

Whole-class work

1. Use this demonstration to model good practice for setting up and monitoring experiments. This will help children to understand what causes rusting and which types of materials can rust. It requires observations over a week, and should be planned appropriately to ensure subsequent lessons benefit from secure conclusions to this experiment.

2. If possible, set up five glass jars, each with a sample of a material in them, such as an iron nail, a steel paper clip, pieces of plastic, wood and aluminium.

3. Label each of the jars to show what is then added:
- Water
- Boiled water with paraffin on top (a tight lid will suffice if the jar is full)
- Nothing
- A sachet of silica gel (and a lid on the jar)
- Water with salt added

4. Over the course of the week ask the children to note and/or photograph changes to the material, keeping a *diary* of events.

5. After a week enough changes should have occurred in some of the jars to enable some meaningful discussions.

6. Ask the children to consider whether the following statements are verified by their findings:
- Iron and steel both rust, but aluminium, wood and plastic do not.
- Both water and air are needed to make iron or steel rust.
- Salt speeds up rusting.
- Iron rusts faster than steel.

Differentiation
- Photographing the jars twice a day will help children appreciate the rates of change. Also, allow them to handle the rusted items and see if they can safely remove any rust. *What does it smell and feel like?*
- To challenge thinking, ask the children to find out what oxidisation involves and means.

Science in the wider world

Scientists call rust *iron oxide*. It is formed when iron reacts with oxygen in the presence of water. We can say the iron has oxidised. Salt speeds up the reaction because it dissolves in the water and helps to *break down* the iron.

Although rust can be removed using wire brushes or acid, rusting is an irreversible change – the rust cannot be turned back into iron.

Review

Conclude the work with a true or false quiz: Scientists call rust iron oxide. (true) Water and oxygen are needed for iron to rust. (true) Salt slows down the rusting of iron. (false) Steel rusts because it is made from iron. (true) Aluminium is a metal that can rust too. (false) Plastic does not rust. (true)

Finally, stress that rusting is an irreversible change, though not necessarily unpreventable. This is the focus of the next lesson.

Objectives
● To know how to prevent rusting.

Resources
Photocopiable page 172 'The rust report'; iron nails; paints (water-based or otherwise); Vaseline, glass jars, cling film; water; packets of silica gel; ICT access (optional)

Speaking scientifically
corrosion, iron, oxidise, oxygen, rust, salt, reaction, galvanise

Lesson 2: Preventing rust

Introduction

If possible, introduce the lesson in role as a vain, self-important business man/woman. Explain your predicament to the class: you have had an enormous 30 feet high iron statue made of yourself, not realizing that it can rust! Even worse, you have to transport it by sea all the way back to your own country. As such, you need scientific help – a scientific report to tell you the very best way to stop your statue rusting. Announce that there will be a reward for the most successful solution!

Recap on findings from the previous lesson, focusing on the causes of rust. Emphasise how anxious you are about transporting a statue the size of a house across the sea as it will be near to lots of salt water.

Group work

In groups of around four, ensure that everyone understands the task. Distribute the photocopiable sheet to each group, and show them all of the materials at their disposal.

Allocate around three nails to each group to allow a range of experiments. As with the previous lesson, the children will need several days to monitor their experiments.

With their experiments complete allow the children time to prepare reports (using ICT if desired) and finalise their presentations. They should also consider how they will translate their findings to practical recommendations for the transportation of the statue.

> **Differentiation**
> ● Allow children different roles for their presentations – some may prefer to operate slideshows or hold up relevant information while another speaks, for example.
> ● Challenge children to say how they would translate their findings into realistic care for the statue, providing information on how the transportation would take place, even researching costs if appropriate.

Science in the wider world

Although iron is immensely strong, its ability to rust can cause many problems. As such, rust prevention is big business. Certain paints are available, but have to be renewed regularly. Plating iron involves putting a thin coat of non-rusting metal over the iron, such as chromium and zinc plating. When iron is coated in zinc we say it is *galvanised*. Stainless steel is a special type of steel that is made by melting and mixing iron with other metals such as chromium and nickel; it does not rust at all.

Review

Back in role, invite the groups to make their presentations to you, allowing time to ask them questions and probe their understanding. If desired, choose a winner.

To conclude, recap that iron rusts when water and oxygen are present, and can be prevented from rusting by keeping it near to a substance that absorbs water from the air, such as silica gel. Alternatively, iron can be coated with paint, grease or oil to stop air and water getting to it, and where that will not suffice, iron can be *galvanised* with zinc, or melted and mixed with other metals to create stainless steel, which does not rust.

■SCHOLASTIC

Objectives
● To understand the processes and work involved in using iron beneficially.

Resources
Media resource 'The effects of rust' on the CD-ROM; a selection of books with content on the uses of iron; internet access

Speaking scientifically
construction, industry, iron, rust

Lesson 3: Iron in everyday life

Introduction
Display the media resource 'The effects of rust' on the CD-ROM, and use the images to recap on the learning from previous sessions. Explain why iron sometimes rusts, and what things can be done to prevent it.

Focus on the related vocabulary and check that the children understand the meanings of key terms such as corrosion and oxidise.

Group or paired work
1. Explain that you want children to research the uses of iron in everyday life. Remembering their work from previous lessons, encourage the children to use books and the internet for their research.

2. To get things moving, brainstorm key questions that might help to structure their research, such as:
- What is iron?
- Where does it come from?
- How is it made?
- Why is it useful?
- What is it used for?
- What difficulties does it cause?

3. Before they start working in earnest, consider the types of presentation they might develop, such as a written report or a slideshow with commentary. Remind all groups of the time limits you are placing on them (one to two hours is suggested).

Differentiation
● Research and provide useful web links for children who might struggle to do this on their own. Encourage them to develop and practise oral presentations.
● For those who need a real challenge, invite them to research manufacturing processes for iron and related products, such as stainless steel.

Science in the wider world
Cast iron has been used to make buildings and structures for centuries, although it became popular in Britain in the 19th century. Today, beautiful cast-iron architecture can be seen all over the world, although it is rarely used these days, partly because of some catastrophic failures (it does not bend or stretch very well, and of course can rust.) Structures like the Eiffel Tower (wrought iron, with carbon mixed in) and the Forth Bridge (the first steel structure in the UK) show how engineering was progressing.

Iron still counts for the majority of the entire world's metal production, and it has a wide range of uses.

There is even iron in our bodies – we need foods that are iron-rich to keep us healthy.

Review
Allow pairs or groups time to hone their work with each other, checking coverage and providing advice on the language used, imagery and factual accuracy.

As children deliver their presentations note the effective use of vocabulary and accurate presentation of facts. Ask appropriate questions to stimulate further ideas, thinking and research.

Develop a display of children's work alongside the experimental equipment and artefacts from the rusting work of the previous two lessons.

Objectives
• To learn how polymers are created.
• To understand the effect of temperature on the initial reaction.

Resources
A selection of plastic items; several litres of whole milk; white vinegar; a large saucepan; a stirrer; a source of heat; a large bowl; sieves; newspapers; tools and table coverings that you might use for working with clay; paper towels; webcam or video camera (optional); modelling clay (optional)

Speaking scientifically
casein (pronounced k-seen), polymer, polymerisation, reaction

Lesson 1: Milk plastic

Introduction

Introduce the children to three new words:

- casein: a protein found in milk
- polymer: a compound made of chains of molecules
- polymerisation: a chemical reaction to form chains of molecules.

Whole-class work

1. Note: try this out before the lesson to help you understand the process and activity it involves. The intention is to make some *milk plastic* (or casein) that will be divided up amongst the class. As such, consider the amount of casein you want to produce. This will be smaller in volume than the original volume of milk. The suggested ratio of milk to vinegar is 16:1.

2. Gather the class so that everyone can see. Use a webcam or video camera to project the activity to your whiteboard if desired.

3. Pour the desired amount of milk into a saucepan, then heat the milk slowly, stirring regularly. When it starts to become very warm turn off the heat, immediately add the vinegar and stir it in. The milk will immediately start to become blobby. Stir for about another 30 seconds.

4. Slowly and carefully pour the milk through a sieve. Shake the sieve to remove excess fluid, but avoid pressing as it will stick in the mesh.

5. Tip the remaining substance onto a waterproof surface (with newspapers around it); you should now have a rather soggy lump of casein. Explain that this has formed because the protein in the milk meets the acid in the vinegar: the casein does not react and starts to lump together – it has polymerised.

6. Put the casein through the sieve one more time, or use paper towels, to dry it out a little more.

Independent or paired work

7. This task provides children with a tactile experience of a freshly made substance. Give the children some casein. Invite them to mould it into a shape – this may be purely experimental (a perfect cube), decorative (simple jewellery) or functional (a drink mat).

8. Encourage the children to consider how they might mould their shape, providing them with absorbent materials to remove excess moisture.

9. If you want them to have a comparison, when they have made their artefact provide the children with a similar amount of modelling clay and ask them to make a copy, then watch the two dry out over subsequent days.

10. Once artefacts are made, ask the children to write up the process involved in making the casein and their experience in using it. This task should continue, diary-like, until the artefacts have hardened.

Differentiation
• Support children by providing a simple cloze text of the demonstration and process.
• To challenge children ask them to plan an experiment that investigates the conditions for producing the ideal casein (even if it is not possible to perform it).

Science in the wider world

Casein is used widely in the manufacture of plastics, adhesives paints, foods and even textiles! It comes from the Latin word *caseus*, meaning cheese.

Review

Once children's artefacts have dried out (which may take several days) gather the children together and share their work and experiences. Invite volunteers to read their recount of the demonstration and their experience in moulding the casein.

Objectives
● To investigate the properties of plastics and compare them to other materials.

Resources
A bicycle (optional, as stimulation); a wide selection of different plastic items, from food packaging to sturdy items and toys; a selection of non-plastic items covering a range of materials including wood, material, metal, paper and card; samples of materials in basic form; equipment suitable for classroom testing of stretching, soaking, scratching, and so on; internet access (optional)

Speaking scientifically
absorbency, elasticity, hardness, plasticity, polymer, properties, stiffness, strength

Lesson 2: Understanding plastic

Introduction
Display a wide range of everyday objects. Around half should be plastic and the other half of cloth, wood, metal, and paper/card. Discuss the items, what they are made of, and why particular materials have been used. Consider whether they are *natural* or man-made. Discuss how they might change under certain conditions, such as exposure to force, temperature or water.

Remind the class of the term polymer, and explain that plastic is typically a polymer, often (but not always) made from petrochemicals.

Group work
1. With the children in groups of around four, explain that an *entrepreneur* is hoping to create a brand-new bicycle made from plastic. They, as scientists will be required to carry out a range of tests on plastic and other materials, leading to a report which they can deliver in any way they wish. Their job is to show how plastic may be good or bad for the different functions of a bicycle, comparing it with other materials.

2. Discuss what bicycles have been made from over the years. Ask the children to consider what properties of plastic may be beneficial on a bicycle.

3. Demonstrate to the class a number of properties they might wish to test:
- absorbency – whether it absorbs water
- elasticity – how flexible it is
- hardness – how resistant it is to scratches and pressure
- plasticity – how much it can have its shape changed
- stiffness – how much can it resist changing shape
- strength – how much load it can take.

(Note that some, such as plasticity, are hard to test for and should be identified by current day uses.)

4. Next, indicate the equipment available for testing the materials. Explain that there are a number of different tests that relate to these properties, such as scratching, stretching, and soaking. Discuss safe and meaningful ways that plastic and other materials could be tested.

5. Ideally, allow the groups to have occasional access to the internet to research information they feel they cannot find through tests.

Differentiation
● Group children appropriately, ensuring that group work guidelines ensure everyone will have meaningful roles. Encourage them to develop presentations that play to everyone's strengths. Encourage effective speakers to deliver the oral element, with others can display images or artefacts to tie in with what is being said.

Science in the wider world
Manufacturers all over the world, whether making toys or trucks, packaging or planes, are interested in materials and their properties. They want to ensure that materials are safe, suitable for their purpose, and as cheap to use as possible. Over time the properties of naturally-occurring materials such as wood and rock have been understood and used, leading to more complex manipulation of materials such as mineral extraction and the creation of synthetic materials. New materials are still being investigated and created, such as graphene, a one-atom-thick layer of graphite that has a wide range of uses.

Review
As a class, invite each group to present their findings and recommendations, allowing the other groups to question them as desired. Use prompts to try and extend reflective thinking.

To conclude, consider the properties of plastic as identified by the class, and consider these against the properties of other materials.

Resources
Photocopiable page 173 'Scientists: Ruth Benerito and Leo Baekeland'; books about scientists; internet access

Speaking scientifically
researcher, polymer, synthetic

Lesson 3: Ruth Benerito and Leo Baekeland

Introduction
Remind the children of their work over the course of this topic, discussing the experiments they have performed and what they found out. Consider the difficult aspects of the work as well as the most satisfying moments.

Remind them of the milk plastic they made, and consider how this was first discovered. *Was it by accident or by carefully considered trial-and-error?* Point out that scientific discovery can come from both.

Whole-class work
1. Display or distribute photocopiable page 173 'Scientists: Ruth Benerito and Leo Baekeland' and read through it with the class, clarifying any vocabulary or ideas as necessary.

2. Brainstorm the implications of the scientists' discoveries. Look around the room and consider any artefacts that may have come from the work of these people, if not actual objects, then things that subsequently derived from them.

3. Remind the children that these scientists were working with materials, as the class has done throughout this topic.

4. Explain that there are scientists working in fields, such as medicine, biology, space and computing. Also remind them that sometimes inventors are not scientists; they simply have ideas to improve lives, such as efficient hand-driers.

Independent work or paired work
5. Explain that the children have to find out about one or more famous scientist working with materials. They can base their work around Benerito and Baekeland, or they can try to find out about someone new.

6. Emphasise that their work can be presented in any way they wish, but should include key information: name, birth date and nationality, field of research, key discoveries and how they happened, uses in everyday life.

Differentiation
● Support learners by asking them to use the photocopiable sheet to create a quiz for their parents/carers to answer. Ideally they should add one or two further questions based on the work they have done in preceding lessons.
● To extend learning, ask children to investigate what the next generation of scientific inventions will be and how they might impact on future lives.

Science in the wider world
For many thousands of years human beings have investigated and manipulated the world around them. The adaptation of reindeer antlers for weapons or the use of herbs to relieve pains is as valid an invention as modern plastics and medicines. The big difference nowadays is that the cumulative effect of scientific discovery, coupled with the extraordinary potential of the internet to transmit and store knowledge, means that many people are starting to understand the world at a molecular level, even for our brains.

A wide range of scientists have had dramatic effects on the way the world has changed, and this is set to continue, with the world continuing to change significantly in the space of a single generation.

Review
Gather the class and ask them to share their work, conducting pair reviews. Bring everyone together and consider what they have found out. Leave enough time for the class to consider the importance of scientists, prompting discussion with questions, such as: *What is the most significant scientific discovery? Are scientists more important than doctors? Can scientific discovery be unhelpful? Can you think of a discovery that would really help people today?*

Objectives

● To explain that some changes result in the formation of new materials, and that this kind of change is not usually reversible, including changes associated with burning and the action of acid on bicarbonate of soda.

Resources

Photocopiable page 174 'Irreversible changes that involve heat'; interactive activity 'Fizz, bang, sizzle' on the CD-ROM; media resources 'Firefighters in action' and 'Burning: before and after' on the CD-ROM; all resources and materials involved in previous heating and burning experiments from week 3

Working scientifically

● Using simple models to describe scientific ideas.

Irreversible changes involving heat

Revise

● Create a vocabulary wall of associated words and ask the class to check and write definitions for them, such as: *boil, burn, change of state, carbon, carbon dioxide, combustion, exothermic, evaporate, evaporation, fuel, gas, hazards, heat, irreversible change, molecule, non-flammable, oxidise, oxidisation, oxygen, solid, change of state, reversible change, reaction, vapourise.*

● Work through the 'Fizz, bang, sizzle' interactive activity to recap basic knowledge.

● Review the experiments and demonstrations that involved using heat:
  ● invisible ink
  ● baking bread
  ● making biscuits
  ● burning materials
  ● burning candles
  ● milk plastic.

● Consider the role of heat in each of these cases, discussing its effect, but also the health and safety implications, reminding children of the serious hazards involved in using heat sources and hot materials, burning, scalding and so on. Use this as an opportunity to reinforce health and safety issues in and around the home.

● Look again at the images on the media resource 'Burning materials: before and after' and discuss the changes to the materials.

● Recap on the role of oxygen in burning, and how firefighters overcome this. Watch the 'Firefighters in action' media resource to reinforce this.

● Mention also the experiment using carbon dioxide to extinguish a flame.

● Remind the class that plaster is exothermic: it generates heat as it dries, and can be dangerous.

● Challenge children to write a story that involves three instances of materials changing state through heating that affects the plot.

Assess

● Provide children with photocopiable page 174 'Irreversible changes that involve heat'. Look for answers that give coherent, well-structured explanations using the correct vocabulary to good effect.

● Where answers are incorrect or weaker, be sure to differentiate between children's gaps in factual knowledge and whether or not they have not understood the processes involved.

Further practice

● Try to provide as much hands-on experience as possible.

● If you have videoed the experiments and demonstration, ask children who need support to watch them without sound and try to supply running commentaries about what is happening.

● Alternatively, supply photographs or drawings of sequences of events in heating experiments, and ask the children to sequence and caption them.

● There is commercial software available that simulates the cooling, heating and burning of materials, which can be useful for reinforcing the different temperatures at which materials change state or burn.

Objectives
● To explain that some changes result in the formation of new materials, and that this kind of change is not usually reversible, including changes associated with burning and the action of acid on bicarbonate of soda.

Resources
Photocopiable page 175 'Irreversible changes that do not require heat'; media resource 'Volcano' on the CD-ROM; media resource 'The effects of rust' on the CD-ROM; all resources and materials involved in previous experiments that do not involve heating and burning from week 5

Working scientifically
● Using simple models to describe scientific ideas.

Irreversible changes that do not require heat

Revise
● Create a vocabulary wall of associated words and ask the class to check and write definitions for them, such as: *acetic acid, corrosion, dilution, distilled water, iron, oxidise, oxidisation, oxygen, carbon dioxide, density, non-flammable, reaction, rust, salt, steel.*
● Review the experiments and demonstrations that did not involve using heat:
  ● making plaster of Paris
  ● making and collecting carbon dioxide
  ● investigating acid strength
  ● making a volcano
  ● understanding rust
  ● preventing rust.
● Recap that although heat is not required to make plaster, the reaction with the water can generate heat because plaster is exothermic.
● Remind the children how to collect gases, asking them to explain the differences between methods for collecting gases lighter and heavier than air.
● Review the model of a volcano using vinegar and bicarbonate of soda, prompting children to consider its strengths and weaknesses as a model. Look again at the media resource 'Volcano' on the CD-ROM, and model vocabulary and processes for the class.
● Look again at the media resource 'The effects of rust' on the CD-ROM, and discuss knowledge and examples from real life. Use cloze texts and Q&A sessions to reinforce vocabulary and processes, including rust prevention.
● Recap the meaning and uses of polymers, and consider how acetic acid reacts with milk to form casein.

Assess
● Provide children with the photocopiable sheet. Look for answers that give coherent, well-structured explanations using the correct vocabulary to good effect.
● Where answers are incorrect or weaker, be sure to differentiate between children's gaps in factual knowledge and whether or not they have not understood the processes involved.

Further practice
● Try to provide as much hands-on experience as possible, using materials that react together.
● If you have videoed the experiments and demonstration, ask the children who need support to watch them without sound and try to supply running commentaries about what is happening.
● Alternatively, supply photographs or drawings of sequences of events in heating experiments, and ask children to sequence and caption them.
● Ask the children to look out for rust at school and home, noting where it occurs, the severity, and the possible consequences (if any) if it is left untreated.
● Display ranges of materials, including polymers, to let the children freely explore their properties and qualities.

Objectives

● To explain that some changes result in the formation of new materials, and that this kind of change is not usually reversible, including changes associated with burning, oxidisation, and the action of acid on bicarbonate of soda.

Resources

Water; different flours; PVA glue; borax or something similar (optional, see note on health and safety); food colourings; a range of measuring and mixing equipment; newspapers

Working scientifically

● Planning different types of scientific enquiries to answer questions, including recognising and controlling variables where necessary.
● Reporting and presenting findings from enquiries, including conclusions, causal relationships and explanations of results, in oral and written forms such as displays and other presentations.
● Identifying scientific evidence that has been used to support or refute ideas or arguments.

Investigating slime

Revise

● Recap the investigations and experiments carried out during this chapter:
  ● invisible inks
  ● making biscuits
  ● burning candles
  ● acid strength
  ● rust prevention
  ● understanding plastic.
● Consider the changes that took place in each of these experiments and whether they could be reversed or not, considering why.
● Recap also on demonstrations done in class: making plaster of Paris, baking bread, burning materials and making polymers. Consider why these are irreversible changes, modelling vocabulary and explaining processes as necessary.
● Recap on successes and failures, what made the experiments hard to conduct successfully, and how things can be learned even when predictions don't come true.
● Discuss the experimental techniques that make for good science and scientists: clear plans, cooperation, methodical working and sensible conclusions.

Assess

● Set a group task to create the ideal slime. Showing the range of materials and equipment available, explain that the children should plan, perform and write-up an investigation to create the slime that they think is the most suited to its purpose (which they should also define).
● Stress that all initial tests and experimentation should be done using small amounts of substances, and minimal mess is expected.
● This activity is best performed in pairs or small groups, but obviously this makes assessments harder. This can be overcome, to a degree, by asking children to plan and predict alone, then work with others to agree the best approaches to their experiments. They can then write up their methods, results and conclusions individually. In addition, if possible, the activity could be run on a carousel basis and each group observed in action.
● To give an element of meaning to the tests, groups could go on to package and market their slime, and give *dragons' den* style presentations.
● Note that many online websites will suggest using sodium borate (borax) to make slime (or flubber). Note that it is not necessarily a safe substance, and school health and safety policy should be consulted.

Further practice

● Provide model write-ups of simple experiments to help show effective practice.
● Provide opportunities for the children to repeat experiments children have already performed, following instructions if necessary.
● Ensure that the children are aware and have prompts to hand for the different ways of presenting predictions, results and conclusions – in writing, in pictures, orally, using ICT, making models, and so on.

Name: _____

Date: _____

Heating foods

■ Complete this chart for a range of foods.

Aim: _____

Equipment: _____

Food type	Unheated appearance	Heating information	Heated appearance	Reversible change?

Conclusions: _____

I can describe what happens to foods when they are heated.

How did you do?

PHOTOCOPIABLE

■■SCHOLASTIC
www.scholastic.co.uk

Name: _____   Date: _____

Baking bread

■ Complete these instructions using the words listed below. Then cut them out.
Arrange them in the correct order on a sheet of blank paper.
■ Can you illustrate them, or write explanations for what is happening to the
mixture?

Missing words: hot, dough, hollow, water, rise, flour, yeast

✂ -

Leave the dough to _____ for one to two hours.

Tap the loaf when you remove it from the oven. It should sound

_____.

Mix the flour and _____ together then add water.

Place the loaf in a _____ oven, at gas mark 6, for 30 minutes.

Knead the _____ to make it smoother and easy to manipulate.

Press the dough into a baking tin to remove excess _____.

The correct amount of _____ is important to make good-quality
dough.

Name: _____

Date: _____

Burning materials

■ Complete half of this chart before the materials are heated, then the other half afterwards.

Material	Unheated appearance	What will happen if it is heated?	What happened when it was heated?	Appearance after heating

Conclusions: _____

I can explain what happens when some materials are burned.

How did you do?

PHOTOCOPIABLE

Volcanoes

■ Label the diagram to explain how volcanoes work. Then draw a cross-section of your model volcano.

A real volcano
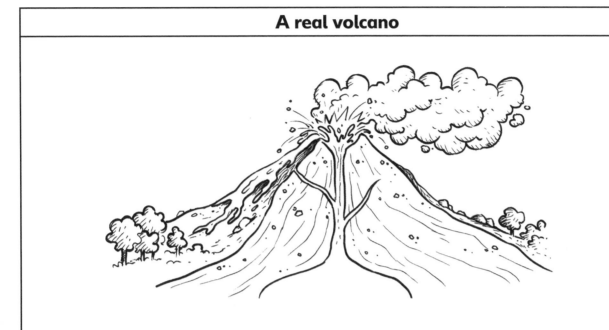
A model volcano

Add any further explanations here: _____

_____

I can describe what happens when a volcano erupts.

How did you do?

The rust report

■ You have been asked to provide help to a super-rich (and rather vain) businessman. He has had an enormous iron statue made of himself, not realizing that it can rust! Even worse, he has to transport it by sea all the way back to his own country.

■ Provide a detailed account of your experiments and provide advice on the best way to stop the statue rusting on its week-long journey across the sea.

Introduction – what the report is about:

Data – present your test results here:

Are the results true and valid? What did you do to ensure a fair test?

Conclusions and recommendations – how can the iron statue be transported safely across the sea?

I can understand how rust occurs and how to prevent it happening.

How did you do?

PHOTOCOPIABLE

■SCHOLASTIC
www.scholastic.co.uk

Scientists: Ruth Benerito and Leo Baekeland

■ Read about these two important scientists and think about what their lives were like. Can you discover anything else about them?

Ruth Benerito is an American scientist, born in 1916. She is famous for inventing wrinkle-free cotton. Cotton had been used for many years for clothing and was grown by many farmers in America, but in the 1930s nylon and polyester, which are synthetic materials, were invented. They were not always as comfortable as cotton but were easier to look after, so many people started switching to them, and the cotton farmers were very worried.

In the 1950s Benerito and her assistants discovered a way of treating cotton fibres so that synthetic molecules 'stuck' to them. This created wrinkle-free cotton fibres, and later led to the invention of flame- and stain-resistant materials.

When Ruth Benerito was 86 she received a Lifetime Achievement Award for her work on textiles and her commitment to education.

Many years earlier, in 1907, Leo Baekeland created one of the first synthetic materials that came to be used so much in modern life.

Baekeland was from Belgium in Europe, but moved to America to study science and to work. His first major invention was a special type of photographic paper. This probably made him quite rich (inventors can patent their work so that no one else can use their discovery without permission): it was reported that his motivation for inventing things was to make money.

Using a special machine (called a Bakelizer) Baekeland and his research assistants created a polymer that was a hard plastic that could be moulded. This led to bright objects that were dyed phenol-formaldehyde plastic, known as Bakelite, which was very popular and widely used for many years.

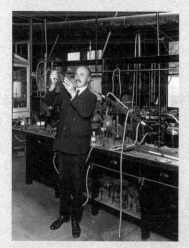

Although modern plastics replaced Bakelite, it is still popular with collectors. There is even a museum for it in England!

Irreversible changes that involve heat

■ Try to answer these questions about irreversible changes that involve heating substances.

1. Ella and Dan put some ice cubes in a pan then put it on an electric hob. They don't turn off the heat until the pan is dry.

a. Describe the different things they will see: _____

_____

b. What safety advice would you give them? _____

_____

2. What is the difference between heating and burning? _____

_____

3. Why does wood give off smoke when it burns? _____

_____

4. Why do candles burn? _____

_____

5. Name three ways that a candle can be extinguished:

a. _____

b. _____

c. _____

I can understand why some materials are permanently changed by heat.

How did you do?

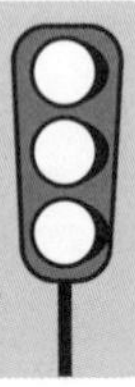

PHOTOCOPIABLE

SCHOLASTIC
www.scholastic.co.uk

Name: _____   Date: _____

Irreversible changes that do not require heat

■ Try to answer these questions about irreversible changes that do not involve heating substances.

1. What happens if vinegar is added to bicarbonate of soda? _____

_____

_____

2. How can you collect carbon dioxide? _____

_____

_____

3. Why does iron rust? _____

_____

_____

4. Explain two or three different things that can be done to stop iron rusting:

a. _____

b. _____

c. _____

5. What is a polymer? _____

_____

_____

6. What is the difference between a natural and a synthetic material? _____

_____

_____

I can understand why some materials can never be changed
back to their original form.

How did you do?

Forces

Expected prior learning
- Understand magnetic forces.
- Know that magnets have two poles.
- Know that some attractive forces act at a distance.
- Know that two like magnetic poles repel each another.

Overview of progression
By the end of this chapter children should have learned:
- how to measure forces
- how to consider the direction of the force and its effects on the motion of an object
- about the forces of friction and the principle of a gravitational field
- about the application of forces through simple machines such as pulleys and leavers.

Creative context
- Application and effects of forces have clear links with the technology curriculum.
- Many children's toys require forces to be used to make them move and provide the interaction.
- There are also links to technology with work on simple machines near the end of the chapter.

Background knowledge
Forces, measured in newtons, are all around us. The Earth's gravitational field, or simply gravity, acts on the mass of a body to give it weight which, if not supported, will pull the object to the ground. The same gravitational field makes objects stay on the ground and not float about. Objects that we want to move are held in place by the force of friction that opposes the motion of any object and will slow the speed of an object if the driving force is removed. Gravity acts at a distance whereas friction is a contact force.

Speaking scientifically
- *Attract* and *repel* are terms used to describe when objects move towards each other or away, respectively. *Mass* and *weight* have specific meanings within science. Whilst we often refer to our weight, the figure we give is usually a mass in kilograms. Mass is the matter we are made of and is constant whether on Earth or on the Moon. *Weight* is the gravitational field pulling down on that mass toward the centre of the Earth. On the Moon, the gravitational field is less and so our weight is less. Two surfaces rubbing on each other cause *friction*; on the other hand an object moving through a fluid, liquid or gas, is subject to a resistive force known as *drag*. Drag can be reduced if the object has a small surface area moving into the fluid, that may steadily increase; think sports car not double-decker bus.

Preparation
You will need to provide: Newton or force meters, magnets, paper clips, pieces of card of varying thickness, skipping rope, modelling clay, screw top bottle, model car, scissors, large glass of water, coin, pin or needle, tissue paper, pencils, magnifying glass, a plumb bob or small mass, string, modelling clay, Plasticine®, balance/scales measuring in grams, several small objects to weigh, graph paper, bathroom scales, material for parachutes, stopwatches/stopclocks, a toy car, trundle wheels, rounders posts, a bicycle (optional), library reference books, internet access

On the CD-ROM you will find: media resources 'Streamlined shapes', 'Simple machines'; 'Bicycle', 'Penny farthing', 'Hit the brakes'

Chapter at a glance

Week	Lesson	Curriculum objectives	Lesson objectives	Main activity	Working scientifically
1	1	• (Y4) To notice that some forces need contact between two objects, but magnetic forces can act at a distance.	• To revise how magnets attract some but not all metals. • To investigate magnetic forces acting at a distance.	Investigating how a magnet can attract materials at a distance through other materials.	• Planning different types of scientific enquiries to answer questions, including recognising and controlling variables where necessary.
	2	• To experience forces that make things begin to move, get faster or slow down.	• To identify different forces and how those forces affect objects around us.	Using forces to change the shape of objects.	• Reporting and presenting findings from enquiries, including conclusions, causal relationships and explanations of and degree of trust in results, in oral and written forms such as displays and other presentations.
	3	• To experience forces that make things begin to move, get faster or slow down.	• To identify where forces are balanced and unbalanced.	Carrying out experiments and making observations to describe how forces affect the movement of objects.	• Reporting and presenting findings from enquiries, including conclusions, causal relationships and explanations of and degree of trust in results, in oral and written forms such as displays and other presentations.
2	1	• To explain that unsupported objects fall towards the Earth because of the force of gravity acting between the Earth and the falling object.	• To identify forces and their direction. • To label forces in terms of size and direction.	Identifying the size and direction of forces.	• Reporting and presenting findings from enquiries, including conclusions, causal relationships and explanations of and degree of trust in results, in oral and written forms such as displays and other presentations.
	2	• To explain that unsupported objects fall towards the Earth because of the force of gravity acting between the Earth and the falling object.	• To know that the force that pulls an object down is its weight in newtons.	Using a Newton meter to measure the weight of different objects. Comparing an object's mass and weight. Using secondary sources to discover that the weight of objects will vary on other planets.	• Taking measurements, using a range of scientific equipment, with increasing accuracy and precision, taking repeat readings where appropriate. • Recognising which secondary sources will be most useful to research their ideas.
	3	• To find out how scientists, for example, Galileo Galilei and Isaac Newton helped to develop the theory of gravitation.	• To use research skills to find out how a scientist developed ideas. • To know that gravity isn't just an Earth phenomenon. • To compare the work of two scientists.	Watching a video clip of an experiment on the Moon. Researching Newton and Galileo.	• Recognising which secondary sources will be most useful to research their ideas. • Identifying scientific evidence that has been used to support or refute ideas or arguments.
3	1	• To identify the effects of air resistance, water resistance and friction, that act between moving surfaces.	• To know that air produces a force that opposes motion.	Discussing streamlining and looking at streamlined objects.	• Reporting and presenting findings from enquiries, including conclusions, causal relationships and explanations of and degree of trust in results, in oral and written forms such as displays and other presentations.
	2	• To identify the effects of air resistance, water resistance and friction, that act between moving surfaces.	• To know that parachutes slow down the speed that an object falls. • To know that the size of a parachute changes how quickly an object falls.	Investigating parachutes and the effect of changing parachute size.	• Planning different types of scientific enquiries to answer questions, including recognising and controlling variables where necessary. • Recording data and results of increasing complexity using scientific diagrams and labels, classification keys, tables, scatter graphs, bar and line graphs.

Chapter at a glance

Week	Lesson	Curriculum objectives	Lesson objectives	Main activity	Working scientifically
3	3	• To identify the effects of air resistance, water resistance and friction, that act between moving surfaces.	• To understand the differences between the resistance to motion of air and water.	Watching a clip of a dive at the Olympic Games. Analysing the shape of divers. Finding out how different liquids resist movement.	• Recognising which secondary sources will be most useful to research their ideas.
4	1	• To identify the effects of air resistance, water resistance and friction, that act between moving surfaces.	• To know that friction slows down movement. • To know that a Newton meter can be used to measure friction forces.	Investigating the different frictional forces from different surfaces.	• Planning different types of scientific enquiries to answer questions, including recognising and controlling variables where necessary.
	2	• To identify the effects of air resistance, water resistance and friction, that act between moving surfaces.	• To know that sports equipment is designed with the need for friction and grip.	Carrying out research to identify the different materials used in sport to give grip.	• Recognising which secondary sources will be most useful to research their ideas.
	3	• To identify the effects of air resistance, water resistance and friction, that act between moving surfaces.	• To identify when high or low friction is needed.	Considering situations where high and low friction is important or consequences when the friction is wrong.	• Using test results to make predictions to set up further comparative and fair tests.
5	1	• To explore the effects of friction on movement and how it slows or stops moving objects.	• To know that drag forces will stop an object unless a force is used to push it forward.	Demonstrating the forces acting on a moving toy car.	• Using test results to make predictions to set up further comparative and fair tests.
	2	• To explore the effects of friction on movement and how it slows or stops moving objects.	• To know that brakes must have high friction to make them effective.	Considering the forces required to make an object stop. Drawing and labelling force diagrams.	• Recognising which secondary sources will be most useful to research their ideas.
	3	• To explore the effects of friction on movement and how it slows or stops moving objects.	• To know how speed and other factors affect how quickly a car can stop.	Investigating the stopping distances for cars.	• Reporting and presenting findings from enquiries, including conclusions, causal relationships and explanations of and degree of trust in results, in oral and written forms such as displays and other presentations.
6	1	• To recognise that some mechanisms, including levers, pulleys and gears, allow a smaller force to have a greater effect.	• To know some simple machines which are used to assist movement.	Looking at simple machines and the idea of effort, load and pivot.	• Using test results to make predictions to set up further comparative and fair tests.
	2	• To recognise that some mechanisms, including levers, pulleys and gears, allow a smaller force to have a greater effect.	• To know how some simple machines make moving a load easier.	Looking at the penny farthing to compare distance travelled by effort and load. Investigating gears and pulleys.	• Recognising which secondary sources will be most useful to research their ideas.
	3	• To recognise that some mechanisms, including levers, pulleys and gears, allow a smaller force to have a greater effect.	• To know how the length of a lever can make moving a load easier.	Investigating how scissors and everyday objects use levers to make our lives easier.	• Reporting and presenting findings from enquiries, including conclusions, causal relationships and explanations of and degree of trust in results, in oral and written forms such as displays and other presentations.
Assess and review					

Objectives
● To revise how magnets attract some but not all metals.
● To investigate magnetic forces acting at a distance.

Resources
Photocopiable page 201 'Magnetic force'; magnets; paper clips; pieces of card

Speaking scientifically
attract, repel

Lesson 1: What do we know about forces?

Previous knowledge
Children should understand that forces need contact between two objects and that some forces act at a distance. They should also understand how the poles on a magnet work and how magnets attract or repel each other, as well as other materials. Children should be able to classify materials on the basis of whether or not they are attracted to a magnet.

Introduction
Everywhere we look there are forces at work. To make objects move or to stay in place, forces are needed. Sometimes we can see where the forces are at work, but sometimes the forces are invisible. As small children, we overcame the forces that meant we could only crawl. We bounced up and down in harnesses and then on our beds. We fell over, we threw things, things fell on top of us! Forces are everywhere. If we have a greater understanding of the forces we can predict with greater certainty what will happen and use forces to make our lives easier. Early man designed simple machines to build the pyramids; modern man builds great skyscrapers and rockets to explore space. We need to know about forces to do this.

Whole-class work
1. Use a magnet to pick up a paper clip. Show the children that the paper clip will actually move towards (be attracted to) the magnet without initially being in contact with it. Say that this shows that the force or pull of a magnet exists beyond the magnet: there is a *magnetic field* around the magnet that is strongest at each pole. For a bar magnet, and a horseshoe-shaped magnet the poles are on each end; however, for a fridge magnet they are on the faces of the magnet.

2. Demonstrate how to use a force meter (0–1N) to measure the force needed to pull the paper clip away from the end of the magnet.

3. Discuss with the children how they could use this equipment to measure how strong the force of the magnet is at different distances.

Group work
4. Encourage the children to think of a way of keeping the magnet and the paper clip a set distance apart. Remind them that magnetic forces can travel through card and paper.

5. Using photocopiable page 201 'Magnetic force' as a guide and record sheet, let the children carry out an experiment to measure the force between a magnet and a paper clip when pieces of card, of varying thickness, are placed between them.

Introducing the new area of study
A magnet has a force field around it and can cause a force on magnetic objects without touching them. This is not the only force field and we are constantly affected by a force field: gravity. This topic looks at how that force field causes objects to move or how we must work against it to lift objects. There are forces that work by contact and are responsible for grip and when this force is too small, things slip out of our hands.

Checkpoint
● Can you describe how magnets attract each other?
● Can you describe how magnets attract magnetic materials?
● Can you classify material based on their magnetic properties?

Science in the wider world

Magnets are used in many devices. Often we cannot see them. A fridge door has a magnet all around the seal in order to keep it closed. Fridge magnets and magnetic letters are used to hold artwork and notes to the fridge door. Magnetic containers are sold for holding herbs and spices in the kitchen. Less obvious are the magnets that are in all motors. Whenever electricity is used to make something move a magnet is used as part of the motor. Headphones and loudspeakers use magnets as do microphones.

Review

Discuss the results of the experiment to establish the idea that a magnetic field becomes weaker as distance from the magnet increases.

Assess whether the children make accurate measurements of the strength of the magnetic force, acting on an object and at different distances from the magnet.

Did they conclude that a magnetic field becomes weaker as you move away from the magnet?

Lesson 2: Forces everywhere

Introduction

In this lesson we are going to establish some of the forces around us, besides magnetism, and what those forces can do. A series of simple experiments demonstrate the main points.

Whole-class work

1. Carefully select two volunteers to hold each end of the skipping rope.

2. Ask the other children to describe the shape of the rope as the volunteers just hold the rope ends without any pulling force.

3. Can the children explain how to make the rope straight? Establish that a pulling force is needed. *Do both volunteers need to pull? What happens if one volunteer pulls harder than the other but neither child lets go?* Explain that the pull force causes tension in the rope; the force of tension travels right through the rope. If both the children and the rope are static then the forces are balanced. If the rope moves left or right then the forces are unbalanced and the rope moves in the direction of the greater force.

Independent work

4. The children record the ideas from the demonstration in their work books.

Group work

5. Give each small group of children a large, single piece of modelling clay.

6. Ask the children to share out the modelling clay between them. Then ask what they did to the clay to share it out. Agree that pulling or tension forces might have been used or they may have used a twisting force to rip the clay.

7. Encourage the children to record these ideas in their work books or on a group piece of paper.

8. Using the clay, the children can then make a shape of their own choice.

9. When completed, ask them to consider where they used tension or twisting forces. *Did you use push forces to apply pressure to the clay? How did this force affect the modelling clay?*

10. Ask the children to record their ideas as before.

> **Differentiation**
> - Assist less confident children with the key terminology and develop their scientific vocabulary.

Science in the wider world

Pull forces such as tension and push forces resulting in pressure are used to shape materials such as the metal legs on classroom tables and chairs and on car bodies.

Review

Cut out the strips of paper from photocopiable page 202 'Impossible rip'. Ask for a volunteer to hold the ends ONLY and rip it into three pieces in a single go. You may need to repeat this several times as other children may want to try different twisting and pulling techniques. You can also put the cuts on opposite edges of the paper.

Establish that it's not possible! Agree that you need a pulling force on each side of the cuts to rip the paper apart. Once one cut gives up, there is no tension on the second cut. Refer back to the skipping rope demonstration.

To rip the paper into three, fold the paper in half, end to end. Hold the two ends and the fold and pull: three pieces. CHEAT!

Resources
Large glass of water; coin; pin or needle; tissue paper; pencil; magnifying glass; magnet

Speaking scientifically
balanced, unbalanced, weight, gravity, reaction, surface tension

Lesson 3: Balanced and unbalanced forces

Introduction

In this lesson we will consider how objects stay at rest or move, depending on the size and direction of forces on them. Why, for example don't we sink through the floor? Why does a trampoline change shape when we bounce on it?

Whole-class work

1. Ask the children to recall the tug-of-war demonstration from the previous lesson. Ask them about the tension and the size and direction of forces involved. Remind them that if the rope was stationary, the forces cancelled out. We say the forces are balanced.

2. Invite two volunteers to face each other with their hands outstretched, pushing gently against each other. Point out that if one child pushes harder the forces become unbalanced and the 'pusher' moves forwards whilst the other child moves backwards.

3. Place a chair at the front of the class. Ask the children if the forces on the chair are balanced. *Can you describe the forces that are involved?* Explain that the weight of the chair is supported by the reaction force from the floor.

4. Invite a volunteer to sit on the chair. Say that the chair supports the child with a reaction force and the reaction force between the floor and chair increases to react to the additional weight.

5. *What would happen if an elephant sat on the chair? Would there be enough reaction force from the chair?*

6. Explain that if an object starts to move then there are unbalanced forces. Ask the children to imagine that they are standing on a trampoline. Explain that the surface stretches due to the weight on it and starts to move down. It will stop moving when the tension in the rubber cords or springs balances the force from the weight: the forces are unbalanced and then balanced.

Independent work

7. Let the children record the ideas in their work books using words and pictures. Suggest that forces can be represented by arrows; bigger forces have bigger arrows.

Science in the wider world

A children's playground has many examples of forces: the reaction and tension force when you sit on a swing; the forces needed to make the swing move and go higher. When travelling in a lift the force from the floor of the lift changes as you travel from floor to floor. When going up, the force increases when the lift starts to move. When it stops the force is less for a short while. The reverse happens when the lift goes down.

Review

Take a glass of water and place it on a desk in front of the children. *What will happen if I drop a coin into the water?* (It will sink.) Can the children describe the forces? Establish that there is no reaction force to oppose the weight of the coin. *Will metal float?* (No!) Place a square of tissue paper about the same size as the length of a pin or needle on the surface of the water. Agree that it *floats.* Actually, it's being supported by the surface tension of the water. Drop the pin onto the paper. Explain that the pin doesn't sink as it is also being supported by this invisible force that is supporting the paper. With a pencil, carefully push the paper under the surface of the water, working around the pin. The paper will sink and the pin should be left on the surface. (This may take a few attempts; persevere, it does work.) With a close look or through a magnifying glass, the surface of the water can be seen to rise up around the pin. Use the magnet to move the pin around or rescue any that sink.

Objectives
- To identify forces and their direction.
- To label forces in terms of size and direction.

Resources
Video clip of the Red Bull Space Jump (on the internet); a plumb bob or small mass; string; photocopiable page 203 'A plumb bob'

Speaking scientifically
gravity, weight

Lesson 1: Space jump

Introduction

We are surrounded by a force field. This is called the gravitational field of Earth, or more commonly, gravity. This force field attracts all objects towards the centre of the Earth and defines the direction 'down'. Famously, Isaac Newton was said to have watched an apple fall and devised his theories of motion.

Whole-class work

1. Watch the Space Jump video clip with the children.

2. *Why is it that we know exactly what will happen as soon as the man steps off the edge of his platform?* Agree that we are so used to seeing objects fall towards the Earth that we don't give it much thought.

3. Ask: *Why do things fall?* Establish that there is a force called weight. Weight is caused by a force field called gravity pulling towards the centre of the Earth.

4. Ask a volunteer to hold a small mass (such as a plumb bob) hanging on a string. Ask the children to identify the forces acting on this mass. It should be easy for the class to spot the force of gravity giving the mass its weight.

5. Say: *But if gravity were the only force acting on it, the object would fall. Where is the other force?* Agree that the tension in the string provides an upward force.

6. Show this on a diagram, using arrows to show the directions of the forces.

Independent work

7. Give each child a copy of photocopiable page 203 'A plumb bob' and ask them to draw arrows on the diagram of the plumb bob to show the directions of forces.

> **Differentiation**
> - Work closely with less confident children to describe the forces involved using examples of falling objects or those that are supported.

Science in the wider world

The children will be familiar with the need to support their weight in their arms when hanging from trees or gymnastic equipment. If they let go they fall. Isaac Newton was said to have come up with his theory of Universal Gravitation after watching an apple fall from a tree.

Review

Scientists often refer to a centre of mass; non-scientists call it the centre of gravity. This is a point that is supported where an object will balance, for example, supporting a ruler at the centre. Take a child's chair and ask what will happen if it is slowly tilted backwards. Agree that at the point when the centre of mass of the object goes outside the base of the chair legs it will topple over. This occurs because the centre of mass of the object is no longer being supported.

Objectives
● To know that the force that pulls an object down is its weight in newtons.

Resources
Newton or force meters; Plasticine®; balance/scales measuring in grams; several small objects to weigh; graph paper; computer access; internet access; library reference books; bathroom scales

Speaking scientifically
weight, gravity, newton

Lesson 2: Gravity and weight

Introduction
The force field that is gravity can be measured. We can measure force in newtons using a Newton meter. We can measure the force on any object. We call this force weight. So what makes things *heavy*? All objects on or near the Earth are attracted to the centre of the Earth. Even the Moon is attracted to the Earth by a force that keeps it in orbit (like a ball on a string).

Whole-class work
1. Show the children the force meter and hang a lump of Plasticine® from it. Say that the force meter measures the weight of the object. Explain that the weight is measured in newtons and is written *N*.

2. Compare this with the value for its mass found by placing the Plasticine® on a balance.

3. Tell the children that they will repeat this with several objects to see whether there is a link between the weight in newtons and the mass in grams.

Group work
4. Ask the groups to use a force meter to measure the weight of an object, then to find the object's mass by placing it on a balance. They should repeat this for at least six objects.

5. Encourage the children to record the results in a table, then plot a line graph of weight against mass on graph paper (or using a computer). This work will assess children's understanding of weight as a force.

6. Ask the children to use secondary sources to find out what the strength of gravity is on the Moon and on different planets in the solar system.

7. If you think it appropriate, using a set of bathroom scales, invite the children to measure their own mass. They then work out what their weight would be on different planets (by multiplying their mass by the strength of gravity on each planet). Alternatively, use average mass figures for Year 6 children (around 30–35kg).

Science in the wider world
When we talk about our weight, in scientific terms we actually mean our mass, if we are measuring in kilograms. If we want to actually measure weight then it should be in newtons. Weight is the force on our mass due to gravity, which on Earth is 10 newtons per kilogram.

Review
Discuss the children's findings. Ask them what link they have found. Establish that for every 100g of mass, the newton meter will record 1N.

Objectives
● To use research skills to find out how a scientist developed ideas.
● To know that gravity isn't just an Earth phenomenon.
● To compare the work of two scientists.

Resources
Video clip of the hammer and feather drop on the Moon (on the internet); access to research material on Newton and Galileo; materials to create a poster

Speaking scientifically
gravity, weight, drag

Lesson 3: Newton and Galileo

Introduction
Does gravity only happen on Earth? What other evidence is there? Where did all the ideas of forces come from?

Whole-class work
1. Show the video clip of the hammer and feather experiment on the Moon.

2. Ask: *What is different about this experiment on the Moon compared with what happens on Earth?* Establish that on the Moon there is no atmosphere so objects don't get slowed down by the air. However, gravity still pulls the objects downwards.

Group work
3. The children use secondary sources to find out about Newton and Galileo and their experiments and ideas about forces.

4. Encourage the children to collate their information as a series of slides or as a poster.

Differentiation
● Less confident children may need support to identify appropriate information for their research. Groups could be organised to allow children to support one another.

Science in the wider world
Scientists have always followed each other's work; they share their ideas so that others can check their information. Scientists will generate theories and then make experiments to test them. The experiment on the Moon where a hammer and a feather were dropped was carried out to prove that the scientists from hundreds of years ago were correct about the theories they had, even though they were unable to test their ideas directly.

Review
Invite the children to talk through their research with the class. *What were Newton's big ideas? What were Galileo's big ideas? Is it true to say that Newton invented gravity? Whose ideas, Newton's or Galileo's, were more important? We often hear about Newton but should we celebrate Galileo's work more?*

Objectives
● To know that air produces a force that opposes motion.

Resources
Media resource 'Streamlined shapes' on the CD-ROM: natural, for example fish, and manufactured, for example racing cars

Speaking scientifically
drag, air resistance, streamline

Lesson 1: Going for gold

Introduction
What is it like walking in windy weather? Establish that the wind pushes you around because it puts a force on your body from different directions. *What do you feel on your face when you cycle around the park? Does that change as you change speed?* Say that the children's faces push into the air. The faster they go, the more air is pushed into per second. This force is called drag or air resistance. How do the children change position on their bikes to make cycling into the wind easier? It is not uncommon for them to duck down to reduce the area that is presented to the wind. This is a method of streamlining.

Whole-class work
1. Ask the children if they can identify streamlined shapes, both in the natural world and manufactured.

2. Show the children the photographs on the media resource 'Streamlined shapes' on the CD-ROM. Ask what advantages these streamlined shapes have and why this can be important to some animals which are shaped like that.

3. Invite the children to use secondary sources to put together a display of streamlined objects and add appropriate comments to explain why streamlining is necessary.

Science in the wider world
4. The world of sport and transport are full of examples where streamlining is vital to gain or maintaining speed or reduce the fuel or energy used. Formula One cars are designed to cut through the air but importantly their shape helps to push them down on to the track, the total opposite of plane wings which create lift, a force that opposes weight. Large lorries have large air deflectors on the roofs of the cabins in order to make a bulky vehicle more aerodynamic and to use less fuel. Some lorries are now less rectangular in order to further help reduce fuel consumption. Cycle racers use specially shaped helmets, bicycles and wheels to limit their drag.

Review
Review the kinds of shapes that are streamlined. *Does the direction of movement affect whether a shape is streamlined?* Discuss the importance of streamlining in sports such as cycling and skiing, and how the athletes change their body shapes to become streamlined.

Objectives
● To know that parachutes slow down the speed that an object falls.
● To know that the size of a parachute changes how quickly an object falls.

Resources
Three different sized parachutes made using plastic bags or light cotton fabric and string; paper clips; Plasticine®; stopwatches/ stopclocks; computer access with data handling software

Speaking scientifically
drag, gravity, air-resistance, fair test

Lesson 2: A safe landing

Introduction

This lesson investigates, through experiment, the effect of drag on different sized parachutes. Show the children the three parachutes, using paper clips as the 'load'. Make it clear that they are of different sizes, but each is carrying the same mass. *Why is this important?* Agree that it is necessary for a fair test to take place. *What other factors must be kept the same to make a fair test?* (same height, same shape of parachute, same length of strings, same material for parachutes)

Group work

I. Ask the children to carry out a fair test to examine the experiment in more detail. They should make parachutes and load each one with a couple of paper clips.

2. Using a stopwatch or clock, the children then measure the time taken for each one to fall to the ground from a constant height (about 1.5m).

3. Encourage the children to put their results into a scatter graph or bar chart. This is a good opportunity to use data-handling software to transfer data from a spreadsheet to a graph.

4. The children should then write a conclusion about what they have found out from the experiment, and what patterns they have observed in their results. Encourage them to give a scientific explanation of these results, using their knowledge of forces.

5. Finally, ask them to evaluate the experiment, looking for possible problems and errors in it, and suggesting how they might improve it, perhaps giving tips to a future group. Use this work to assess children's understanding of air resistance and their ability to carry out an investigation.

> **Differentiation**
> ● Support less confident children to make accurate measurements and collate them in a table. The transfer of data onto the computer may also need support.
> ● Challenge more confident children to make repeat measurements and then calculate an average. You may need to help them create a table to record this information and the correct calculation of the average should be checked if a calculator is used. If using spreadsheet software, the children may need to be shown how the software can calculate their average with the appropriate instruction.

Science in the wider world

Jumping out of planes with a parachute is a dangerous activity! It is important that the parachutes are the correct size to give enough drag or the landing speed will be dangerous. It is also important that the strings do not get tangled or the parachute won't open correctly. Tandem jumps, where two people jump connected to the same parachute, are larger to cope with the extra forces. Parachutes are also used to slow down drag racing cars.

Review

Drop each of the parachutes in turn, asking a child to time each fall carefully. *What do you notice about how the larger, middle-sized and smaller parachutes compare?* Agree that the largest parachute takes longest to fall and the smallest takes the least time. Ask the children to explain these results, using their knowledge of forces.

Discuss their explanations: gravity pulls all the different parachutes down with equal force (because they have virtually the same mass), but larger parachutes have a greater drag and therefore experience less overall downward force.

Note: Some anomalous results may be due to the fact that drag is speed-dependent. Different-sized parachutes will take different times to reach their terminal velocity (the maximum speed of the parachute, when the gravitational and drag forces are balanced).

Objectives
● To understand the differences between the resistance to motion of air and water.

Resources
Photocopiable page 204 'Sinking slowly'; video clip of an Olympic diver; Plasticine®; water; paste; clear plastic tumblers/bowls

Speaking scientifically
drag, air resistance

Lesson 3: A big splash

Introduction
In this lesson, ideas from gravity and drag are combined to consider how falling objects change speed as they fall and how different materials resist motion.

Whole-class work
1. Show a video clip of a diver at the Olympic Games. *How does the shape of the diver change?*

2. Ask the children to describe the shape of the diver as they hit the surface of the water. *Why is this shape so important?*

Independent work
3. Ask the children to work through photocopiable page 204 'Sinking slowly', analysing data on different-shaped pieces of Plasticine® falling through different liquids to decide whether there is high or low drag in each case. Use this sheet to assess their understanding of drag.

4. The answers are: 2. Dome in paste. (The dome is the least streamlined shape – encounters most resistance– and the paste is more resistant to movement through it.) 3. Cone in water. (The cone is the most streamlined shape – encounters least resistance – and the water is less resistant to movement through it.) 4. Paste. 5. Cone.

Science in the wider world
Streamlining is a major factor in the design of cars, boats and planes. Those vehicles with a high drag require more force to move through the air/water which in turn requires more fuel. This has an environmental impact and costs more too.

Review
Ask the children to imagine walking into a strong wind. How would their walking be affected if they were carrying an open umbrella or a very large piece of card?

Objectives
● To know that friction slows down movement.
● To know that a Newton meter can be used to measure friction forces.

Resources
Newton meters; children's shoes and trainers brought in to test; access to a range of surfaces; graph paper

Speaking scientifically
friction, force, grip, opposing forces

Lesson 1: Don't slip!

Introduction
We have looked at the effect of the resistance of motion by liquids and gases. What about the resistance of solids? Without solids opposing motion upon each other, laces wouldn't stay tied, and walking would be impossible. Two surfaces move against one another all the time. When we walk the grip between our shoes and the surfaces means we don't slip over. The force that gives us this grip and opposes the motion is called friction. As we start to try and move an object the friction holds it in place and keeps increasing until the applied force is too great for the friction force for the two materials that are in contact.

Group work
1. Each group pulls their test shoe across different surfaces using the Newton meter. A range of surfaces from desks, floors, sandpaper and other materials around the classroom can be investigated, but it is important to identify the material rather than the object that it is made from.

2. To keep the test fair, the children need to attempt to pull the shoe at a constant speed once it is moving to note the force on the meter.

3. In a table, the groups record the force when the shoe starts to move, or is moving.

Whole-class work
4. Collate the results from the different groups to compare evidence. *Which surfaces gave the highest friction value?* Do all the groups agree? *Which is the lowest value?* Using the group results, can the children identify the shoe type with the lowest friction?

Independent work
5. Encourage the children to create a bar chart with their group's results to show the results of the materials and the force of friction they provide.

> ### Differentiation
> ● Assist less confident children with making and recording their results. Suggest a table design to make recording data clearer. Provide help with creating their bar chart, suggesting labels for the axes and the scale.

Science in the wider world
There are many different surfaces to be found around a school and in the wider world. They are sometimes chosen for aesthetic reasons and sometimes to provide extra grip. For example, stair edges are sometimes made from a different material to the main part of the step, and road surfaces near traffic light or roundabouts have a more textured surface to allow vehicles to brake better.

Review
Discuss with the children how the weather might change how much grip they have when running in the playground or for cars driving on the roads. *Why are 'Caution – Wet Floor' signs important?*

Objectives
● To know that sports equipment is designed with the need for friction and grip.

Resources
internet access; library reference books

Speaking scientifically
grip, friction, surface

Lesson 2: Get a grip

Introduction

Why do we wear special shoes for PE? Why is it dangerous to run on the smooth hall floor in socks. What is special about the different surfaces found on sports equipment?

Discuss with the children how, before starting their gymnastic routine, a gymnast uses a special powder to dry their hands. *Why do you think they do this?* Agree that by doing this, the gymnast is more confident that their hands won't slip off the equipment.

Group or independent work

1. Invite the children to research different sports and consider how grip is important and how it is obtained.

2. Ask them to compare the equipment used in different (but similar) sports and how it affects how the game is played. For example, fluffy tennis balls and tennis rackets compared with smooth table tennis balls and rubber-faced table tennis bats.

3. They could also look into why there are studs on football boots, the grips on goalkeepers' gloves, rounders bats, and so on.

> **Differentiation**
> ● Assist less confident children in finding pictorial ideas rather than relying on printed material.

Science in the wider world

There are many examples of sports equipment having specialist surfaces. The surface of a snooker table has to give the right amount of friction to allow the balls to roll true and the players to skilfully spin and curve the ball. Curling is played on ice that is specially dimpled so that the 'stones' travel further down the ice. Artificial football and hockey pitches have different layers of material below them and are regularly topped with sand to give the right bounce and feel.

Review

Invite the children to present their findings to the class. Compare their ideas and discuss common features.

Have any of them considered or discovered the highly-specialised design of football boots? These days, they are designed not just for their fit but to enable the player to curve the ball by making it spin.

Objectives
● To identify when high or low friction is needed.

Resources
An ice cube; piece of wood of about the same size; media resource 'Bicycle' on the CD-ROM

Speaking scientifically
friction, lubricant

Lesson 3: Friction

Introduction
Sometimes grip is important. Sometimes it is important for things to slip.

Whole-class work
1. Discuss some *sticky situations*, for example when tops can't be removed from jars or when rings get stuck on fingers. In these situations, friction is too large and makes life tricky.

2. Show the children the media resource 'Bicycle' on the CD-ROM. Ask them to identify parts of the bicycle where high friction, grip, is required and other parts where low friction, slip, is needed.

Independent work
3. Encourage the children to generate lists of grippy situations and slippy situations.

Science in the wider world
This lesson has its primary focus on examples from the real world. In order for monkeys to climb trees it is important that they can grip the branches. Snakes have small, rough scales that help them to grip the ground. Trains have smooth steel wheels and run on smooth steel tracks but there is enough friction because of the weight of the train, except when the track is icy. In winter special trains spread sand and salt onto the tracks to improve grip. Wet leaves in autumn also cause problems for trains and delays to journeys.

Review
Invite the children to read out some of the situations on their lists and discuss their suggestions. Are there any similarities and differences?

Objectives
• To know that drag forces will stop an object unless a force is used to push it forward.

Resources
Toy car, video clip of curling (on the internet)

Speaking scientifically
drag, friction, streamline

Lesson 1: Having a rest?

Introduction

Friction and drag both act in a direction against the motion that creates it. To move an object we must provide a force greater than the force of friction. If we remove that propelling force, an object will continue to move but the opposing force will bring it to a halt.

Whole-class work

1. Push a toy car along a desk or the floor. Ask the children to describe the movement. With each stage of the movement ask: *What forces are on the moving car?*

2. Discuss with the children what happens if they stop pedalling when they are cycling. Agree that they slow down. If they don't start pedalling again they slow down so much that they stop and might fall over.

3. Show the video clip of a curling competition. It has many opportunities to examine forces. Ask the children questions like: *Why don't the curlers fall over? Why can they slide? Why do they sweep the ice? Why does the stone stop even on the ice?*

Independent work

4. Encourage the children to write an account of a cycle ride, including what happens when they pedal and stop pedalling. They should also include the forces involved and use the correct scientific terms.

> **Differentiation**
> • Less confident children may prefer to draw diagrams and annotate with a few words, for example, pedalling hard – speeding up, stop pedalling, starting to slow down – drag force.

Science in the wider world

Kicking or rolling a ball in sport gives the ball an initial force but this force is no longer there once the ball is not in contact. Top quality sports people develop their skills to work out how hard to hit the ball so it slows down and stops exactly where they want it, for example in snooker and bowls.

Review

With the whole class, discuss the skills of different sports. Why are some skills based on moving the object as fast or far as possible, for example a penalty kick, and others about placing it carefully, for example a golf ball?

Objectives

● To know that brakes must have high friction to make them effective.

Resources

Media resource 'Hit the brakes' on the CD-ROM; photocopiable page 205 'Hit the brakes'; video clips of a falling ball with hands waiting to catch, a bicycle going downhill, an ice skater on a rink, downhill skier, speedboat on a lake, drag racing car deploying its parachute

Speaking scientifically

speeding up, accelerate, slowing down

Lesson 2: Hit the brakes

Introduction

Display media resource 'Hit the brakes' on the CD-ROM to show examples of items in motion. Without a forward force, a moving object will slow to a halt. Often, we want to control when we stop. In order to do so, we must apply a force to oppose the motion. This is usually done by applying a brake. This is an additional frictional force.

Whole-class work

1. Discuss with the children how we slow down a bicycle. Establish that we usually apply the brakes. *What force is acting between the wheel rim and the brakes?* (friction) *How do we increase the braking power? What happens in the wet? What is the effect of travelling faster on how easy it is to stop? What happens with the front and rear brakes? What happens if you brake hard and the track surface is loose?*

Independent work

2. On photocopiable page 205 'Hit the brakes', the children identify the movement that is in the picture and describe what must be done to stop the object.

Differentiation

● Support children to identify where the forward motion is and therefore identify the force in the opposite direction.

Science in the wider world

The brakes on most bikes apply a frictional force between the brake block and the wheel rim. More expensive, competition-style mountain bikes often have 'disc brakes'. These brakes are near the centre of the wheel which means that they are less likely to become affected by water which would act as a lubricant, or get clogged up by mud. The build-up of mud would provide a friction force slowing the wheel down when you may want to be going faster.

Review

Go through the children's responses on the photocopiable sheet to identify the forward motion and the braking or resistance forces.

Objectives
● To know how speed and other factors affect how quickly a car can stop.

Resources
Data on typical stopping distances (on the internet); trundle wheels; rounders posts; materials for creating posters

Speaking scientifically
stopping distance, thinking distance, braking distance

Lesson 3: Stop!

Introduction

When crossing the road we must always look and listen out for traffic. We must never run out in front of a vehicle after a friend, a ball, and so on; vehicles cannot stop instantaneously when they are moving. But how far does a car travel when it is slowing down? Why are car speed limits important and why is it important for cars to travel slowly near a school?

Whole-class work

1. Using the data on stopping distances, measure out with a trundle wheel on the school playground the distances needed for cars to stop. Leave a couple of children at each stopping point. Tell the children that they are creating a living graph.

2. With rounders posts or similar, ask the children to leave a labelled marker at each point.

3. Gather the children together. Ask them for their reactions to the distances. *Are you surprised by how far the cars will travel before they stop?*

Independent work

4. Invite the children to design a poster to display around the school promoting road safety. Encourage them to include the words used in the lesson.

> **Differentiation**
> ● Some more confident children may wish to use word processor software to produce their words for their poster to enable a *professional finish* and make their work more presentable.

Science in the wider world

It is important that we recognise how far it takes for vehicles to stop and that at higher speeds these distances increase. Understanding the concept that stopping instantaneously helps us to make decisions as to how close to drive behind another vehicle or whether the car we are in can stop before the line when the lights change. This could be particularly important at pedestrian controlled lights that the children might use on their journey to school or when the crossing warden steps out into the road.

Review

Discuss with the children that the distances marked out in the playground are minimum distances. Can they explain how these distances would be affected by icy or wet conditions? Encourage them to use scientific words in their explanations.

SCHOLASTIC

Objectives
● To know some simple machines which are used to assist movement.

Resources
Media resource 'Simple machines' on the CD-ROM; paint can; a screwdriver

Speaking scientifically
effort, load, pivot

Lesson 1: Effort and load

Introduction
We are surrounded by simple machines. A machine is a device that makes doing mechanical work easier, that is, using less force. Early humans used simple machines to move objects that couldn't be moved by strength alone.

Whole-class work
1. Explain to the children that the effort is where we apply a force and that a load is the force we must work against.

2. Show the children the paint can with its lid on. How could they get the lid off? Allow some guesses before revealing the screwdriver. *How does this help?* Show the children where the effort (where you push down), the pivot (where the screwdriver is on the edge of the can) and where the load (the friction force holding the lid on) is.

3. Open the media resource 'Simple machines' on the CD-ROM. Invite the children to identify where the load and effort are in each situation.

Group work
4. Encourage the children to identify the load and effort on simple machines around the room/school or in their home.

> **Differentiation**
> ● Support the children to identify levers around the room. Scissors, door and window handles all apply a force using a pivot.

Science in the wider world
From scissors and shears to cranes and bulldozers, all these machines use forces in different places to their point of contact on an object. The force and effort are in different places.

Review
Gather the children together and discuss their ideas and examples. Check that they have correctly identified the efforts and loads.

Objectives
● To know how some simple machines make moving a load easier.

Resources
A bicycle; media resources 'Bicycle' and 'Penny farthing' on the CD-ROM; Internet access; library reference books

Speaking scientifically
gear, effort, load

Lesson 2: Gears and pulleys

Introduction
On a bicycle the pedals are used to apply the effort against the load that is forward motion through a gear. Pulleys are used to lift loads that without the pulley would be much too heavy to lift. Sailing boats have pulleys to lift the sails and haul in the anchor. Modern cranes use a series of gears and pulleys to lift loads around a building site.

Whole-class work
1. Using the bicycle or photo of one, show the children that bicycles have different sized cogs on the pedal cog compared with the wheel cog. Ask the children if they can explain why.

2. Then show the children the media resource 'Penny farthing'. Discuss the size of the pedal turn compared with how far the wheel turns.

Group work
3. Invite the children to use the internet or library books to investigate uses of gears and pulleys.

Differentiation
● Assist less confident children in identifying the most useful sources of information.

Science in the wider world
The idea of gears is not a modern phenomenon. Windmills used cogs and gears to transfer the force from the wind on the sails to direct the motion to the right places in the windmill to grind the grain or lift the bags of grain around the mill itself.

Review
Bring the children together to discuss their findings and compare the ideas and information gathered in their research.

Objectives
● To know how the length of a lever can make moving a load easier.

Resources
Newton or force meters; 'slinky'; smaller springs; spring-loaded suction cup toy

Speaking scientifically
lever, pivot, effort, load

Lesson 3: Levers and springs

Introduction
We are surrounded by levers and springs and in this lesson, we are going to find out more about them. Scissors are examples of levers. Early humans used a simple lever to lift heavy rocks. Show the children the suction cup toy with the spring in the base. Explain that we need to use a force to compress the spring. The spring stores the energy used when we compress it. When the suction is insufficient, the object *springs* into the air. The children may also have trampolines that have springs that stretch.

Whole-class work
1. Ask for a couple of volunteers. In a clear space, ask them to carefully pick up their chair. *Is it heavy? In which direction is the force?*

2. Ask the children to move the chairs slowly until they are holding them out in front of them. It is unlikely that they will reach full stretch. *Has the chair got heavier?* Ask why they cannot hold out their chair in front of them. Establish that the *machine effect* is working against them. With their arms outstretched, the force is further from their shoulder joint which is a pivot, or turning point for the force. The effect is called leverage, and the simple machine is a lever.

3. Now talk about springs. Point out that when we turn a door handle it returns to its normal position. *Why is this?* Establish that there is a spring inside the mechanism of the handle. Explain that springs produce a force when stretched or compressed from their normal position. Tell the children that inside the Newton meter there is a spring that is stretched to read the value of newtons.

Group work
4. Invite the children to use Newton meters to measure the force needed to turn different levers. Door handles and doors have pivots or hinges that a force can turn about. There are also brake levers on bikes. Can the children identify the pivot, effort and load? *How does the force change if it is applied at different distances from the pivot?*

Science in the wider world
Long spanners are needed to move stiff bolts as there is more turning force; the pivot is the centre of the bolt. To lift up a manhole cover, we might use a long crowbar to lever off the cover. The pivot is the edge of the manhole.

A mattress on a bed contain springs. We squash the springs when we sit or lie or jump on the bed. It gives a pushing force back in the opposite direction to our weight.

Review
Discuss with the children the principle of levers and how long levers make it easier to turn objects. *Can you think of any examples we haven't yet mentioned?* They may have seen taps for elderly and disabled people which have long arms. These are useful to people who may not be able to give sufficient force to turn a shorter tap arm.

Objectives
● To explore the effects of friction on movement and how it slows or stops moving objects.

Resources
Photocopiable page 206 'Skidding and slipping'

Working scientifically
● Reporting and presenting findings from enquiries, including conclusions, causal relationships and explanations of results, in oral and written forms such as displays and other presentations.

Skidding and slipping

Revise
● Recap the effect of the resistance of motion by liquids, solids and gases.
● Friction and drag both act in a direction against the motion that creates it. To move an object we must provide a force greater than the force of friction. If we remove that propelling force, an object will continue to move but the opposing force will bring it to a halt.
● Discuss with the children the impact of different surfaces and how the weather might change how much grip they have when running in the playground or for cars driving on the roads. Ask: *Why are 'Caution – Wet Floor' signs important?*

Assess
● Provide the children with photocopiable page 206 'Skidding and Slipping'.
● Invite them to identify the correct word to complete sentences about friction.
● In the second part of the sheet, the children have to identify situations where the friction is high or low and say why that is important.

Further practice
● Prior to completing the photocopiable sheet, discuss with the children ideas about frictional forces and what factors influence them.
● To extend the activity, children can create their own scenarios to identify the different forces.

Objectives
● To recognise that some mechanisms, including levers, pulleys and gears, allow a smaller force to have a greater effect.

Resources
Model construction equipment; Newton meters; hanging masses

Working scientifically
● Taking measurements, using a range of scientific equipment, with increasing accuracy and precision, taking repeat readings where appropriate.
● Reporting and presenting findings from enquiries, including conclusions, causal relationships and explanations of results, in oral and written forms such as displays and other presentations.

Lifting the load

Revise
● Remind the children that a machine is a device that makes doing mechanical work easier, that is, using less force. Early humans used simple machines to move objects that couldn't be moved by strength alone.
● A lever is a device that involves a rod or pole in relation to a pivot point. Using a lever allows us to move a large weight using a small amount of effort. If you use a lever to increase the distance moved, the force needed is more. If you use a lever to increase a force, the distance moved is less.

Assess
● Working in small groups, set up the construction equipment so that one end of a single long piece of modelling material is pivoted at one end. Lift the other end with a Newton meter.
● Position hanging masses at different points along the rod, and record the force on the Newton meter.
● The children record the measurement of the force on the Newton meter and the position of the hanging mass from the pivot.
● They write a conclusion to explain the pattern.

Further practice
● Support the children in designing an appropriate data table.
● More confident children could hang the mass at the end of the rod and record the force on the Newton meter as it is used to lift the mass when placed at different positions along the rod. They could also use a graph plotting program to display the results.

Objectives
● To explain that unsupported objects fall towards the Earth because of the force of gravity acting between the Earth and the falling object.
● *To explore the effects of friction on movement and how it slows or stops moving objects.*

Resources
Hardboard slope; such as a clipboard; toy car; metre rulers; 30cm rulers

Working scientifically
● Planning different types of scientific enquiries to answer questions, including recognising and controlling variables where necessary.
● Taking measurements, using a range of scientific equipment, with increasing accuracy and precision taking repeat readings when appropriate.
● Recording data and results of increasing complexity using scientific diagrams and labels, classification keys, tables, and bar and line graphs.
● Reporting and presenting findings from enquiries, including conclusions, causal relationships and explanations of results, in oral and written forms such as displays and other presentations.

Speedy slopes

Revise
● Remind the children of Isaac Newton and what he deduced from watching an apple fall from a tree.
● Discuss how gravity acts on the mass of a body to give it weight which, if not supported, will pull the object to the ground.
● Remind the children that friction and drag both act in a direction against the motion that creates it. To move an object we must provide a force greater than the force of friction. If we remove that propelling force, an object will continue to move but the opposing force will bring it to a halt.

Assess
● Working in small groups, explain to the children that they are going to carry out an investigation into the link between the height of a slope as a car starts and how far the car can travel beyond the end of the slope.
● The children can measure the height that the car falls down a fixed angle of slope as one factor and measure the distance travelled.
● Look out for fair testing and repeating results for higher levels of achievement

Further practice
● To support the children, remind them about the force that makes the car fall and the force that slows down a moving object and how those forces affect the motion of the toy car.
● More confident children could consider changing the angle of the slope and maintaining the dropping height, or simply different angles of slope against distance travelled.
● Alternatively, they could consider different surface materials for comparison. Ask: *Do the rules linking height fallen and distance rolled apply equally to all surfaces?*

Magnetic force

Number of pieces of card	Force needed to pull paper clip off magnet N

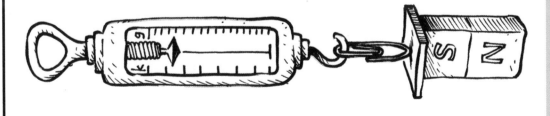

I can measure the force between a magnet and different thicknesses of paper.

How did you do?

Impossible rip

■ In one go, tear this strip of paper into three pieces!

PULL →

Cut/
Rip

Cut/
Rip

PULL →

PHOTOCOPIABLE

■SCHOLASTIC
www.scholastic.co.uk

A plumb bob

■ Draw arrows on the diagram to show the direction of forces.

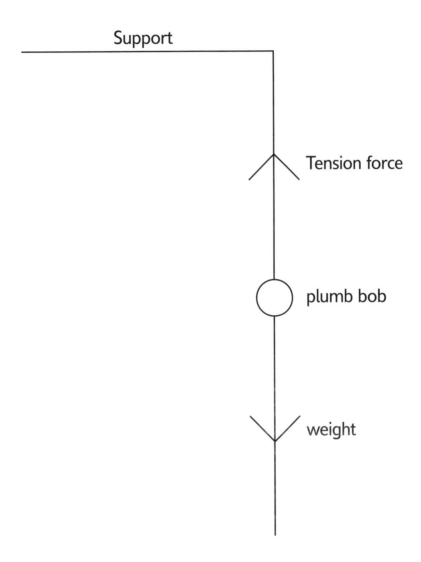

Support

Tension force

plumb bob

weight

Sinking slowly

Shape	Time taken to fall through paste (seconds)	Time taken to fall through water (seconds)
ball	2.5	1.0
-	3.0	2.0
cone	2.0	0.5
cylinder	3.5	1.5
cube	5.0	2.0
dome	6.0	2.5

■ This table shows the results for an experiment using several objects, water and wallpaper paste.

1. Plot two bar charts to show the two sets of results.

2. Which shape takes the longest to fall, and in which liquid? _____

through _____

Explain why this is. _____

_____

3. Which shape falls through the fastest, and in which liquid? _____

through _____

Explain why this is. _____

_____

4. Which liquid has more drag? _____

_____

5. Which shape falls faster through paste than the dome falls through water?

_____ Explain why this is. _____

_____

I can see how different liquids resist the movement of objects.

How did you do?

Name: _____   Date: _____

Hit the brakes

■ Identify the movement that the picture is showing. Describe what must be done to stop the object.

I can explain what needs to be done to stop something moving.

How did you do?

Skidding and slipping

■ Choose the correct word from the brackets by crossing out the wrong words.

When you try to move an object or an object is moving, a force tries to slow it down or stop it. This is called (gravity/electricity/friction/grip).

When there is (high/low) friction it is hard to move the object and go (fast/slow). If there is (high/low) friction it is easy to move an object and go (fast/slow).

There is _____ friction

between the ice skate and the ice

because the ice is _____.

There is _____ friction between the nut and bolt. This is important

because _____

_____

_____.

We need _____

here because _____

_____

_____

_____.

I can describe different types of friction and how they affect movement.

How did you do?

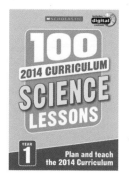

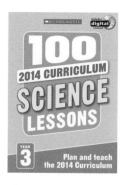

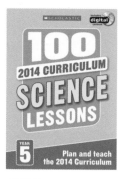
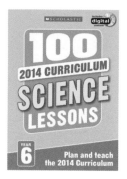
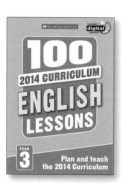
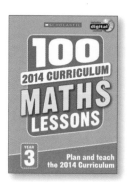
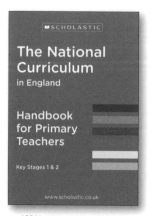